My Journey
Towards Healing
Battling Lyme Disease

D1488519

Terry Diener

by TERRY DIENER

ISBN: 978-0-692-92901-8

Design by: Leah Miller

Carlisle Printing
OF WALNUT CREEK LTD

800.927.4196 · carlisleprinting.com
Sugarcreek, Ohio 44681

Dedication

I dedicate this story to Julie. As a couple we face life together and it is because of her that I am on a journey towards healing. She was relentless in researching for answers for my health problems. There were times when I wanted to give up, but she was persistent. I cherish her love, care, and wonderful spirit.

I am grateful for my children: Lindsy and her husband Joe, Eric, and Casey who have been understanding and encouraging over the years of many strange health issues. They never questioned my sanity but were present to offer words of care and support. Without their love I would not have had the motivation to continue to look for solutions.

I dedicate my story to my grandchildren: Michael, Julia, and Sophia. They are the joy of my life and although they do not know it, their presence in my life has brought an important kind of healing.

Acknowledgments

There are a number of people to whom I want to express my appreciation for their efforts in helping to write my story. First and foremost, I am greatly appreciative of my editor, Karen Sheriff LeVan, who read the document many times and made great suggestions that helped my story come to life. She poured her expertise and passion into this story and was so much more than what I expected from an editor. I am indebted to her, and without Karen this would not have been possible.

I am grateful for Alyssa Kauffman who proofread the first very rough draft. I appreciate my family members who read my story and gave feedback: my mother in–law Bertha Bontrager Rhodes, my sister Marlene Boese, my brother Ron, and Julie's cousin Renette Borton. Thank you for your loving care and sensitive and helpful comments. There were several friends who also read my story in the early stages and gave me encouragement and the belief that it was worth sharing.

But above all I am thankful for my wife Julie. Julie not only supported me but spent hours reading my story in the early stages and giving advice. She wrote from her own experience as well.

Introduction

I am a tick magnet. I will never know why they love me so much. I love being in the woods and walking through tall grasses. Unfortunately, these are the places the ticks love as well. So, it is not unusual for a tick and me to make a connection.

There have been a few times when my wife Julie has awoken in the morning to find a tick crawling on her. That is a major event and she always blames me for bringing the tick to bed. I have never convinced her that just maybe it came with her. The good news is that those we find have not yet embedded themselves into our bodies. But, over the years I have found a few of the little devils only after they had buried their head under my skin. So, I do not know which one it was that had a dirty mouth and infected me with a truly horrible disease. But that one little bite changed my life as a middle-aged man. Seventeen years later, I am hopefully in my last phase of grueling treatment.

Sometimes Lyme disease is called the "invisible disease." And some refer to chronic Lyme disease as "the disease that does not exist." I can think of several names to call it, and none of them are very nice. It is a disease that is difficult to diagnosis because everyone's symptoms are varied and the medical establishment will not recognize chronic Lyme disease. For me, it was a 12-year journey of weird health issues that seemed to have no good answer until I finally heard the words, "Mr. Diener, I am 100% sure you have Lyme disease and we can help you."

I can never overstate the relief of having a diagnosis and the assurance that life can get better.

I have read some stories written by persons who have lived with chronic Lyme. But, I have never read a story written from a male perspective or from a faith perspective. This is partly what prompted me to write my journey towards healing: to be a voice for men whose health is failing and who are trying to live with the desperation that weakness and fatigue brings. It is a disease that raises such tough questions and extreme emotions. Am I sick, or am I lazy? Am I sick, or am I depressed? Am I sick, or am I going crazy? And where does this rage burning inside of me come from? I write this story to be a voice for all who are living with health crises that have no good answer and so the frustration builds.

I write this story too for the many family members and loved ones who suffer as they walk with someone who is so sick and help is slow to come. In more ways than I know, my family, like the families of many others, has lived and is living with chronic Lyme disease as well. "From Julie" sections at the end of several chapters honor and clarify the multifaceted, shared nature of this experience. The same is true of my sister Marlene's "Foreword." Together, we share our stories to be advocates for the much-needed research into more effective diagnostic tools and treatment strategies.

Writing has also been one more way to continue healing. As I've recalled my story I am once again reminded of all the special people, moments, and blessings from God that have brought me hope and joy in the midst of the storm of battling Lyme. It is healing to be able to share my story with others.

Foreword

My brother Terry and I, along with our three other brothers, grew up in a loving family with parents who modeled God's love, grace, and peace. Our parents left a legacy of love and the assurance that we walk by faith in God's presence. Even as young children we knew that as a family, and as part of God's family, we experience God's love in the good times and the bad. We grew up knowing we are loved. But we also grew up knowing that sometimes we experience difficult challenges along the way.

Mom once told me that because she needed help with the babies, Terry was often designated as her helper. Maybe that is why very early on Terry and I developed an extraordinarily close brother-sister bond. It must have been the hours of bottle feedings and entertaining Marvin and me while Mom took care of household chores. Or maybe it was all the times Terry let me crawl into his bed for protection during a powerful Kansas thunderstorm. For all these reasons and more, Terry and I have a deep genuine connection.

After Terry and Julie returned from their three year volunteer assignment in Brazil and settled in Goshen, Indiana, Terry suggested that we start calling each other on Sunday evenings. We have been making those calls for over thirty years. Through countless phone calls we have shared life's secrets, joys, and struggles.

For the past seventeen years, I have been walking an extraordinary journey with Terry. In the winter of 2000 during our weekly phone calls, Terry would mention his unusual fevers, headaches, and fatigue. Terry was often reluctant to share how he felt because he knew I worried and carried his pain. But, over time he was willing to honestly answer my probes and share the details of years of illness. When Terry was finally diagnosed in October 2012 with Lyme disease, it was a huge relief, but it was only the beginning of a never-ending journey. With Julie by his side, a church full of prayer warriors, and supportive children and extended family, Terry walked his Lyme journey by faith.

I am forever grateful to Julie for being relentless in her search for answers and determined to restore Terry's health. I am in awe of her attention to every detail in Terry's care. I have seen her love in action as she devotedly cares for Terry both physically and emotionally on this journey. Terry would not be where he is in his healing process without Julie.

To the church members of Clinton Frame Church, thank you for your love, patience and compassion that you generously extended to my brother Terry. He would often mention how grateful he was for the understanding and support extended to him during the necessary medical leaves. He was deeply humbled by the encouragement, concern and prayers of his congregation. Your prayers have been experienced in God moments all along the journey.

I am thankful to Dr. Jemsek for dedicating his life to the research and treatment of Lyme. He has given life back to my brother and thousands of other patients.

Thank you, Terry for opening up yourself to share your story with others. My hope is that your narrative will increase support and compassion for people living with chronic Lyme disease and other chronic illnesses. My prayer is that it will help improve their treatment and their lives.

Thank you to readers for opening your hearts and minds to Terry's story. May it make all of us wiser and more mindful of life's vulnerabilities. May it bring hope to those who suffer from chronic Lyme disease or whatever the challenge in life might be. May it make all of us stronger and kinder.

-Marlene Diener Boese, March 1, 2017

Before

My wife, Julie, says that among the many reasons she fell in love with me was my work ethic. I'd grown up on a Kansas dairy farm where there was always work to do. My siblings and I had several hours of chores beginning early in the morning. We'd feed calves and milk cows before and after school. I also developed a love of hunting as a boy. Any spare time we could find, my brother Ron and I went hunting for pheasants, prairie dogs, and jackrabbits. To this day, my brother Ron, who also now lives in northern Indiana, and I still spend a lot of time deer hunting together.

Working and spending time outdoors in general connects me to the earth. Physical labor invigorates me, and I still keep a hobby farm. The sweat of felling trees, cutting logs and cleaning up the tops is exactly how I love to spend an afternoon.

Julie and I married in 1975. We met at Hesston College in central Kansas where she received her degree in nursing. After I graduated from Wichita State with a degree in Social Work, we decided to volunteer three years with Mennonite Central Committee, a relief and community development agency of our church denomination. From 1980 through 1983, we loved working alongside our Brazilian neighbors in a brutal subtropical environment in the northeast state of Pernambuco. Julie taught health classes and worked with a local agency in training rural health workers. I helped communities hand dig around 50 wells. The wells we dug were up to 30 feet deep, using shovels and picks to dig through clay and stone until water was found. We'd lower concrete rings three feet high and three feet across, into the hand dug wells. Once completed with a concrete lid and hand pump, many families in each community would have clean, healthy water. This is the kind of hard physical labor I find incredibly rewarding.

After our return from South America, I worked on a construction crew: framing, roofing and finishing homes. Our daughter Lindsy was born in Brazil, and after moving back to the United States, we added two sons, Eric and Casey. In the mid 1980s I became co-owner of a construction business, and shortly thereafter, began studies to become a pastor. I attended Associated Mennonite Biblical Seminaries receiving my Master of Divinity degree. These were busy years.

During seminary studies from 1990 to 1994, I was a full-time stay-at-home dad in the summer months while Julie worked as a nurse. I loved being an active dad. I coached little league soccer teams for many years while our children participated, and was also active in 4-H, helping each of our children in showing beef, poultry, rabbits or sheep at the fair.

By the time Lindsy was 16, Eric 14, and Casey 12, Julie was campus nurse at a local college, and I was living my calling as a Pastor of a large thriving congregation. Pastoring brought on a new form of physical stress and emotional work, but I loved being a pastor. I took on the long hours and different job situations with the same stamina as I'd dug wells in Brazil years earlier.

One afternoon I visited an elderly woman in our congregation who was dying and sat with her family. From there I went to the hospital to visit a young couple who was celebrating the birth of their second child. I treasure a job where you get to be involved in the lives of people from birth to death. Pastoral care brings me great fulfillment. Even as early as high school I felt a calling to church ministry.

We kept a small farm with cattle to satisfy the farmer in me, and I was enjoying life to its fullest. Julie and I planned to build a new home on our dream location, a property we'd purchased well off the road and in a wooded area with a swamp we could dig out for a pond. I spent the summer of 1999 clearing a spot for us to build, relishing the joy-filled challenge of cutting over 40 large hickory trees and cleaning up countless smaller trees and brush. Smells, sights, and sounds of the woods bring me peace.

We moved into our new home in January 2000, and it was that winter that I started running a low-grade fever that didn't go away for four months. At age 46, I developed flu-like symptoms and fatigue that I just couldn't shake. This was the beginning of a devastating blow to my sense of self.

I made several visits to our family doctor who could find no good explanation for the fever or fatigue. Fatigue reshaped my life for the first time. I would go home occasionally in the middle of the day to rest, something that was totally out of character for me. I pushed through, but I was always tired. And the fatigue lasted. One summer when I traveled with our church's youth group to a convention, I couldn't keep up with the group and marveled at how fast they walked without tiring. More frustrating yet was my inability to keep up with the other adult leaders.

One afternoon I attended a seminar for sponsors put on by a nationally known youth ministry speaker. What I really wanted to do was go to my room and crash, but I didn't let myself. The speaker was entertaining, funny, and thought provoking, but it wasn't long until I had fallen asleep. I woke up close to the end of his speech. He had talked about the story from Luke 7 of the woman who anointed Jesus' feet in the home of the Pharisee Simon. He told us to turn to another person and tell them which character in the story we related to the most. I turned to my sister, Marlene, who was also attending as a sponsor from her church, and said "I'm the broken jar. I just feel empty." I had no idea what was going on with me, nor that I would continue to feel this way for years.

Julie and I agree that we try to live as equal partners. But during the years before we knew what was wrong, and when I was too tired to move, that sense of equality was sometimes very difficult to find. I lost connection to many of the activities that made me whole. It became very difficult to enjoy hard work, take care of the farm, keep up with the kids, and all physical outlets that had kept me in touch with the earth and with myself. I was doing what I needed and wanted to, but without the enjoyment. We were losing the life we knew, and couldn't figure out why.

---

from Julie:

Our children still remember their childhood years with fondness when Terry was at home full-time during the summer. Our daughter, Lindsy, remembers doing fun things like going bowling. Terry told the kids if their scores totaled more than his that he would take them to Dairy Queen. If their scores didn't beat his, they would go to Dairy Queen anyway. A lot of time was spent outdoors and in the barnyard with animals. It seemed as if Terry and the kids ganged up weekly and brought yet another animal onto the farm. Animals included donkeys, angora goats, geese, chickens, a nest of baby skunks that were trapped at a friend's home, bottle fed baby raccoons, a pony with a cart, and the cows with baby calves. Inside animals included hamsters, a white rat, a turtle, lovebirds, a cat and others. Our farm really became more like a zoo.

Terry was energized and enjoyed his years in Seminary. Some of our friends during college informed me that Terry would someday become a pastor, so I wasn't at all surprised when that's what he ended up doing. We went into our marriage open to whatever God might call us to do, whether in a church setting or elsewhere. And we've always been supportive of one another's work as parents and as professionals.

I enjoyed watching Terry's ministry evolve. His strength in pastoral care and counseling was evident and we could see the usefulness of his Social Work degree. We soon grew to love the people of Clinton Frame Church as they encouraged and embraced Terry in his various roles on the pastoral team. Eventually he would become lead pastor. During these years, we felt we were right where God meant for us to be. Little did we know at the time what a gift God gave us by placing us into this faithful community that would pray and care for us through the many difficult years ahead.

During the first years of Terry's fatigue I talked him into going to an endocrinologist who could find nothing. Even though I had training as a nurse in the medical field, I was raised in a home that practiced alternative modes of health care, so I also talked him into going to a chiropractor and at one point to an Iridologist—a practitioner that studies the color patterns and characteristics of the iris—to gather information about a person's systemic health. She told us that Terry's liver was in serious trouble and had him do a liver cleanse. We never returned to her, and many years later, we would learn that she was absolutely correct.

At times, I talked Terry into taking Vitamins or some natural supplement. Later on, Terry would do infra-red sauna treatments, IVs for detoxification, lymph massage, detox foot baths and lots of herbals.

As a nurse I wanted to talk about his fatigue and try and figure out what the underlying problem might be. At times this caused tension between us. Terry likely didn't know how to talk about his health, or even how to understand or name how he felt. At times he became defensive and irritable, saying that I was being critical of him. So mostly I quit talking about my concerns, and the issue of fatigue remained unspoken. Preserving our relationship mattered more than addressing the fatigue.

Terry mastered the art of denial during the early years of his fatigue. His work schedule included many evening meetings and very long work days. He managed to do what he had to. He pushed himself through the long days. Then he made it to the kids' sporting and other events, cut wood for our wood burning stove, and kept up with work around the farm, but just barely. I would look into Terry's eyes at the end of the day and see 'an empty man.' Most evenings he would sink into the recliner and barely move a muscle until he forced himself to go to bed. He was not himself.

Beginning

It would be another twelve years before we had a firm diagnosis, but I believe it was probably while I was felling and cutting up trees to clear space for our dream home that I contacted Lyme disease through a tick bite. We cannot know for sure since we had also traveled to Wisconsin and the northeast, areas known for Lyme disease, over the previous years. At any rate, it was the winter of 2000 that my first symptoms of Lyme occurred.

At the insistence of Julie and myself, my family doctor agreed to put me on antibiotics a couple of times. We have wondered if the early treatment of these antibiotics may have been one of the reasons the more critical symptoms were delayed.

With good intentions, our family doctor also prescribed an antidepressant, which thankfully I didn't take since we later learned that individuals with Lyme disease often experience devastating complications from the medication. Almost all Lyme patients are diagnosed as depressed at some point, when their doctor has no other explanation. Often the anti-depressants have horrible side effects and the patient ends up being admitted for inpatient treatment. Others end up committing suicide. It is hard to overstate the desperateness of feeling horrible and being told it is just in your head or that you are depressed, the desperation that can come from wanting to feel better but after many doctor visits still finding no improvement and no hope. This psychological war within one's mind is certainly part of the suffering of many persons with Lyme. Julie and I both knew that depression was not the cause of my problem, which is why I chose not to take the medication.

After several months my fevers went away, and I believe the Lyme bacteria slowly began to infiltrate my body. My main symptom continued to be fatigue. I lacked energy, but I learned I could push through. I worked long hours, but would occasionally hit a wall and crash for a day. Later I became very familiar with that wall, when I simply could not keep going. During these years, I was often frustrated by what I thought was a weakness as I could not keep up with the energy level of others. One morning on a youth service trip to Toronto, Julie insisted that I sleep in, and I felt tremendous guilt and frustration in not being able to do my job.

One symptom of Lyme disease is brain fog, and the years of 2004-2011 are somewhat of a blur to me. I was also doing everything in my power to cover up and deny how I was feeling. I continued to work the long hours for the church, and to work on my farm because I was determined not to let tiredness dictate how I lived. I wanted to be my old energetic strong self. In my heart, I knew something was happening to my body that I could not explain, and that no one else could explain either. As best I could, I fought overwhelming frustration by throwing myself into the busyness of being the father to three rapidly growing kids and working in a job that I loved. While I felt weak and inadequate, I tried not to give in to those feelings.

Once I began having one major health issue after another, I began to take my health very serious, and tried to take as much responsibility as I could. It could have been easy to let Julie take over and communicate in medical jargon with doctors and other nurses. But since I was the patient, she tried very hard to allow me and insisted I have the conversations with the doctor or practitioner. She'd chime in only if I asked or if it seemed I needed backup. Before many appointments, however, Julie coached me how to be brutally honest and detailed about my health. According to her, I tend to minimize or downplay my symptoms. I sometimes tired of these rehearsals, but I did learn to talk medically and clearly communicate my problems and needs.

Going from one specialist to the next, I am thankful Julie was with me to help decipher the medical language. Among the doctors we visited included a neurologist, urologist, endocrinologist, cardiologist, electrophysiologist, retinologist, general surgeon, on top of primary care physicians. Years later when we finally had our first appointment with a Lyme disease specialist, the admission form listed thirteen specialists, and we can recall at least three more physicians we did not put on the list.

---

from Julie:

I believe the severe symptoms of Lyme disease began with Terry's retinal bleed in 2008. Next came the first episode of Brachial Plexitis in 2009. He also had four major surgeries in ten months. He had a Nephrectomy (removal of a kidney due to cancer), repair of the nephrectomy incision, which opened three days later, hernia repair and removal of his gallbladder. At this time especially, his immune system hit rock bottom. Early in 2011, a slow, irregular heart rate began which Terry lived with for over a year, at times struggling with a heart rate in the low 40s. Eventually he had two ablations. Terry also lived with neuropathy (pain and numbness) of both feet for seven years, and had frequent headaches and constant pain in his neck and shoulders. His fatigue was ever-increasing.

Terry often became discouraged, and even angered, as we became used to hearing the words, "there is no reason why this should have happened, you are healthy otherwise." Terry would tell me this, "when you are told often enough that there is nothing wrong with you, you start believing that it must be in your head." I knew without a doubt that it was not in his head and that something was desperately wrong, but we had no medical evidence to back us up. Terry's personality is such that he suffered quietly with very little complaining, even through the many years of treatment when he was at his worst.

Considering the massive amount of medical language involved in blood tests, scans, ultrasounds, MRI's, you name it. Terry had a lot to learn. Considering his lack of energy and time, he did an amazing job at learning as much as he could. Often I would find articles on the Internet to explain an upcoming test, new medication or a new diagnosis, and he would gladly read these to become more informed. I marveled at how compliant he was to any orders, whether it was testing or taking medications. Only once in a while Terry would say that he is done and wasn't going to do something, but I think it was his way of asserting his independence to see what kind of reaction he would get from me. Dependence on me—even temporarily—was sometimes hard to accept. Terry's compliance and determination to learn all he could about his health has made me love and respect him all the more.

During these years, I was having my own battles with menopausal symptoms and serious hormone imbalance. As a result, I had many years of severe insomnia, often sleeping only two to four hours at night. I have shared this with very few persons, but have resolved that there was purpose for this time in my life. As I lay awake for hours beside Terry, wondering what to do next, I started praying. I prayed hours in desperation, not only for sleep to come, but how to get needed help *for Terry. I often believed that he was slowly dying right in front of my eyes and beside me in bed. It was during the long nights that I noticed how shallow and irregular his breathing had become and that he had involuntary jerking of his legs and arms while he slept. I could not believe or accept that the medical world was failing us, and that there were no answers. So I turned to God for long talks at night. I often thought of something to research or a person I could talk with, so I guess my talks with God helped us both.*

A Blur

By the summer of 2011, I realized I was in trouble even though I was determined to try to save the life I loved. I had a health crisis in early July of that year which was a total mystery to me at that time. It was a hot summer day and we had a baptism service at our pond for the morning worship service. Julie and I had spent all week fixing our place up for the around 500 guests we would have that morning. For some reason, we felt like our property needed to look like a well-maintained park for the baptismal service. That Sunday morning my balance was off, and I knew I was not doing well. I was shaky doing the baptisms, but I didn't think anyone noticed. After the service two people asked me how I was feeling, and one said they weren't sure I would make it out of the water. My head ached, and I had overall weakness. That morning for the first time I felt my words were a bit slurred when I preached and led the service. I don't think those listening could have noticed.

After the meal was over and everything was cleaned up, I left on my motorcycle to ride six hours to Pittsburgh for a denominational assembly. Against Julie's wishes, I headed out. She always knew when I was struggling, but she could not talk me out of leaving. I have a stubborn side, a wall I sometimes put up when she is saying something I do not want to hear. She would say it was my male ego that makes me do things like this. I wasn't healthy enough to do it, but I did it anyway. Really, getting on a motorcycle when one's balance is off is not smart. I suffered through that ride, and about halfway to Pittsburgh I admitted to myself that this was pure craziness. But, I didn't stop and that evening finally arrived at the hotel in Pittsburgh.

In the hotel lobby I saw a pastor friend, and we talked briefly. He wanted to talk about how I was feeling, but all I would say was that I was doing fine. Two days later I saw him again and he pushed me hard on how I was doing. Finally, he told me how worried he had been after seeing me two nights earlier. He said he kept thinking about how terrible I looked. I told him that I was really tired that day, but that I had recovered and was doing great. It was so much easier to say that than to try to explain how I really felt. I didn't even understand how I felt myself. The truth was I felt horrible, and I took off every afternoon from the delegate sessions to sleep in my hotel room. I was weak and not able to do what I considered to be just normal activity.

Fatigue is so much of the journey of a person living with Lyme disease. January 2000 is when my fatigue moved in, and it would only get worse during the treatment phase. I recently read an article by Jennifer Crystal in *Lyme Times* (July 2016) entitled "The Debilitating Experience of Fatigue" that voices some of what I understand about fatigue. Every person's journey with Lyme disease is different, but Jennifer's explanation of fatigue hits home for me:

> *Fatigue can mean a lot of things. Muscle soreness after a bike ride. Feeling drained after a long day at work. Droopy eyes, the desire to take a nap, the need for an extra cup of coffee. All of these fit into the category of normal tired. What makes them normal is the base level underlying them. If a person is otherwise healthy, they are able to push through normal fatigue because their adrenals are working properly and their bodies are*

not worn down from fighting infection.

Sick tired is another story. The fatigue of the tick-borne diseases is not a general malaise that can be fixed with a nap or a cup of coffee. It is a crippling flu-like exhaustion, one that leaves muscles not sore but literally unable to function; one that makes the body feel shackled to the bed. It is hard for someone who has never been that sick to understand what a person with chronic tick-borne illness means by saying, "I'm so tired today." I have had well-meaning friends say, "I'm tired a lot too" but in the next sentence they tell me that they're going to the gym or planning a party.

This is especially unfair to patients with chronic fatigue syndrome—a nebulous umbrella under which many people with Lyme disease fall. "Fatigue" is hardly a strong enough word to cover what it feels like when your adrenals are shot, your nervous system has gone haywire and your body refuses to function. Even as a writer, it's hard to articulate exactly what I mean when I use the word exhausted.

It took years of medication, alternative therapies, and hard work to get out of the rut of "sick tired" and battle my tick-borne disease into remission. However, I still have to be very careful about pacing myself, or my "normal tired" can quickly slip into "sick tired." So I take a nap every afternoon. If I don't, I hit a physical, mental and emotional wall, melting down like a small child. Napping for me is a necessity, not a luxury.

My feelings of fatigue have been a bit different, but I resonate with much of what Jennifer Crystal says. What was worst for me was that in the midst of the fatigue, I had a nagging feeling of being weak and frail. I so struggled, not understanding and not wanting to accept the reality of what my body was saying to me.

There were many questions in my mind that I could not resolve. How can a middle-aged man admit that he was too tired to get out of bed in the morning? How could a middle-aged male accept the reality that he could not function and live life like his peers? How can a person feel so awful but all medical tests come back normal? How many times can a doctor not have an answer? What does a middle-aged man do when he fears his physical weakness is just in his mind? How does one admit that? This was a constant battle in my mind, with my emotions, with my own body. Julie would tell me that I needed to listen to what my body was saying, but my mind and will could not accept that. How does a middle-aged man listen to his body?

The other difficulty is that the sense of overall weakness and failing health is impossible to describe to people who genuinely care. I know that many persons battling cancer and chemo therapy experience this dilemma. At one church function, I went over and sat with a dear sister in the church who I knew was losing her battle with cancer. I asked her how she was doing and she said, "I'm doing okay." I told her I simply wanted to know how she was really feeling on this particular day. I genuinely wanted to know. She said, "I will tell you since I know you'll understand. I just feel awful but I don't know how to explain it. I really don't have a fever or a headache today. It is just an overwhelming feeling of weakness that I can't put words to. I feel drained of emotion and motivation. I can't explain it, I feel just awful all over." She went on to say how frustrating it is to try to explain something that she herself does not understand. My heart went out to her, and yes, even though my journey was very different, I knew exactly what she meant. When one is not able to describe the sickness, it is easier to say, "I'm doing fine."

I remember reading a comment written by a person who had suffered from Lyme for many years that has stuck with me. This young woman described living with Lyme as the walking dead. On the outside, she seemed normal and people could not see by looking at her that she was sick, but inside she felt like she was dying.

Now as I look back I can admit that for years I knew something was horribly wrong with me. However, doctors could not find a good reason for how I felt, and at times I questioned if they believed me. It was easy for me to just resolve that it was just in my head which made me question my mental stability. This uncertainty and frustration of feeling weak is a very difficult part of living with the Lyme bacteria that is secretly attacking your health in so many ways. The Lyme bacteria goes into an undercover mode and begins to attack any soft tissue in the body.

It would be another four years before I had the firm diagnosis, but the first obvious result of the Lyme disease I now know was the loss of sight in my right eye in the summer of 2008. Years earlier I had done Lasik surgery on both eyes. As a result, I had monovision. My right eye was used for seeing distance and my left eye for reading. I noticed that my vision was bad when driving but did not discover what was wrong until preaching a funeral sermon.

As I looked to the congregation, people's faces were blurry. Wondering what was wrong, I closed my right eye but the blur remained. When I closed my left eye, the sanctuary went black dark, and I realized that I could see nothing with my right eye. Immediately after the burial I called my optometrist and told him that I had lost sight in my right eye. He saw me the next day and found that I had a retinal bleed which resulted in a pool of blood behind my eye. On Monday I returned to his office for laser surgery which stopped the bleeding. He said there was no way to know how much of my sight would come back, but he'd be surprised if 50% of it returned. This was my first miracle. In a few months I had total sight back in that eye.

I was referred to a retinal specialist in Chicago for further treatment. He told me there were only three possible reasons for a retinal bleed: heart disease, diabetes, or high blood pressure. I did not have any of those illnesses so once again I was told, "Yes, it's true this has happened. We just have no explanation as to why." I would hear those same words from many doctors over the next few years. In her study of the retinal bleed, Julie read that this condition can be caused by Lyme disease. This makes sense since Lyme often attacks the eyes and some people go blind.

Julie, with her ever-present intelligence and research impulse, asked the retinal specialist if my loss of sight could be related to Lyme. He immediately said, "Oh, no, that is impossible." He was the first doctor to essentially deny the existence of Lyme disease. He may not have said it outright, as some doctors would, but it was not at all a serious consideration for him.

I give total credit for the return of sight in my right eye to prayer. I am blessed to be a part of a praying congregation, a congregation that believes in the power of prayer and practices prayer on a daily basis. The power of prayer would be an integral part of my journey through the years ahead as I experienced many "God moments" and blessings in the midst of pain and health crises.

Some Comfort

A person in our congregation who had gone through a very difficult time gave me a devotional book, *Jesus Calling* (2004), that became a lifeline for me. It was written by Sarah Young, who I later learned had herself experienced chronic Lyme disease. When I learned that, her devotional book took on new meaning. These words were written by a woman who had experienced a similar journey to mine. From *Jesus Calling*, June 10:

> *Rest in me, My child. Give your mind a break from planning and trying to anticipate what will happen. Pray continually, asking My Spirit to take charge of the details of this day. Remember that you are on a journey with Me. When you try to peer into the future and plan for every possibility, you ignore your constant Companion who sustains you moment by moment. As you gaze anxiously into the distance, you don't even feel the strong grip of My hand holding yours. How foolish you are My child. Remembrance of Me is a daily discipline. Never lose sight of My presence with you. This will keep you resting in Me all day, every day.*

These are powerful words of hope and comfort for living in the reality of God's presence. Through this journey I experienced God in the tiny coincidences that bring peace. It was easy for me to feel far from God as I struggled with a sickness I did not even know I had. Ally Hilfiger in her book, *Bite me*, wrote what I believe to be very true: "Being sick is bad enough, but being sick and not knowing why is insufferable." I turned to *Jesus Calling* often through the years of facing what I could not understand or name.

I also often returned to one of my favorite Biblical passages which is an invitation from Jesus. Matthew 11:28: *Come to me all you who are weary and are carrying a heavy burden and I will give you rest. Take my yoke upon you and learn from me, for I am gentle and humble of heart and you will find rest for your soul.* What a blessing to be able to rest in the loving presence of Jesus in the midst of weariness and frustrations.

One of the blessings of the retinal bleed was that it led to discovering that I had renal cell cancer, better known as kidney cancer. The retinal specialist ordered a heart scan to make sure I did not have heart disease. Fortunately, my heart was clear, but they detected a shadow on my lung. The scan of the lung was clear except for some minor scar tissue, but the scan revealed a shadow on my kidney.

I had a kidney scan and discovered a growth the size of an egg. Our son Casey, who was in nursing school at this point, went with Julie and me to the first appointment to view the scans. Casey noticed some lines that looked like small strings going out of the cancerous growth and asked the doctor what they were. We were informed that the small strings were being put out by the growth looking for nourishment. It was amazing for me to realize how a cancerous growth desires to grow. It was also remarkable to me that Casey would see something I did not. He asked such great questions. This is just one example of the support and care Casey has offered over the years.

One month later I had surgery to remove my right kidney. Fortunately, since it had been detected early, the cancer was contained and did not require further treatment. The kidney cancer probably was not a direct result of my Lyme disease. But my immune system had been weakened which could have allowed the cancer to grow. The surgery was successful, and I was home in three days.

I then had complications that I believe could have been Lyme-related. The first indication of a complication was my inability to eat the first few days after surgery. I have often heard very sick people say that they have no appetite. I always wondered what that meant because it seemed as if all they needed to do was to put some food in their mouth and swallow. How hard could that be? I now know how discouraging it is to have no appetite and be unable to eat. In his good-hearted attempt to take care of me, Casey brought me a medium-size chocolate frosty. This is something that I love to eat. I took one small bite and pushed it away. I could tell he was disappointed, and I was frustrated, but I simply said, "I'm sorry I can't eat it." It is impossible to explain how that feels, so we say, "I just don't have an appetite.

My colon did not wake up after the surgery, which is called an ileus, so two days after returning home I was getting worse, really very sick. I still was unable to eat and was not going to the bathroom. I was miserable, one afternoon I was lying in my recliner when Julie's sister Cindy and my niece Abbi came to visit me. Abbi and I had a special relationship, we loved hanging out together. I overheard Cindy tell Julie, "He must feel really bad. He just ignored Abbi." Later, I became nauseated and due to a Nissen surgery I'd had in the 90s for acid reflux, my esophagus was so tight that I could not vomit. With the dry heaves, the incision from my surgery began to open up, and the next day I was back in the hospital for another surgery to repair the incision.

I woke up from the surgery with a tube up my nose which went to my stomach. My mouth was dry and my throat sore. I just wanted water. But, when I asked, the nurse said I could have nothing to drink. I begged for ice cubes and, after checking with her supervisor, she said I could have two chips. I knew this was going to be a rough few days. I would have nothing to eat or drink for the next five days. This took a huge toll on my body and my already overworked, overwhelmed immune system.

The first night after surgery I was in a lot of pain all night and unable to sleep. I kept pushing my button to receive morphine, but nothing seemed to make a difference. I just thought this was the way it was supposed to be. What kept me going through that night was my Dad's favorite Bible verse, Psalms 121:1. Over and over I heard, *I lift my eyes to the hills, where does my help come from? My help comes from the Lord the maker of Heaven and earth.* That verse sustained me through the long night.

In the morning when there was a change of nurses I told the nurse I was having a lot of pain. She carefully checked the machine and said, "I am sorry, you did not get any morphine all night long." Without looking at her, I managed to say that I had been pushing my button. She very kindly, almost timidly, answered, "I know you pushed it 98 times but something is broken." I could hear her working on the machine, and then she told me. "You are going to feel better soon. I just made up for some of what you missed during the night." She quickly left the room and in a few moments I was asleep.

The next five days I was very sick. Two of the nights Julie stayed with me as I was hallucinating. My body and mind were breaking down. One morning Julie informed me that I spent most of that night trying to figure out how to fix a broken-down truck. The irony is that I am probably the world's worst mechanic. Those were long days and nights.

The timeline for removing the tube from my stomach was simple. When I had a bowel movement it would come out. My sister, Marlene, who believes in reflexology, told Julie where to rub my feet to stimulate my bowels. Julie rubbed my feet for hours in her attempt to get things moving. Sunday morning the hospital doctor came in and said it looks like I would have the tube for at least another 24 hours. He would be back tomorrow to check my progress.

At 8:30 my mind went to the small group at church who I knew were meeting for prayer, and I knew they would pray for me. At 9:30 I thought of the Sunday School classes gathering, and I knew they would pray for me as well. At 9:45 it finally happened. I went to the bathroom. A few minutes later my surgeon came into the room and said, "Well, you kept your end of the deal so the tube is coming out." What a relief that was. The next day I was discharged and went home.

From there I recovered nicely from the surgery and was back to work. However, eight months later I began to develop a hernia at the sight of the incision from the kidney surgery. Once again, I had surgery to repair the incision. The surgeon said that for some reason the wound had not healed correctly; the tissue at the point of the incision had not bonded. He did not know why something like this would happen, but he fixed it by inserting a large piece of mesh. I am sure the incision failed to heal because of my Lyme disease. This was another time when a doctor was baffled and had no good answer.

One After Another

At this point it seemed the Lyme disease took over my whole body. I think that with the surgeries my immune system was even further compromised and now the bacteria were rampant. It next showed up in the spring of 2009 by causing extreme pain underneath my shoulder blade, a condition called Brachial Plexitis or also known as Parsonage Turner Syndrome. There is a center of nerves under the shoulder blade and this was the point of attack. The spiral-shaped Lyme borrelia burrows itself into any soft tissue in the body, especially the brain and nervous system. I had extreme pain for about ten days, with the pain radiating down my right arm and into my hand.

On the fourth day of the extreme pain I visited a woman from our congregation in the hospital who was dying from cancer. I was in so much pain as I met with the family that I called Julie and went straight from the hospital room to the E.R. wanting to know where the pain was coming from. They could not diagnosis the problem, ruled out any problem with my heart, but did discover that I had large stones in my gall bladder. I would follow up on that later.

I tried different things to alleviate the pain. I got a massage which did not help. I went to my favorite doctor, Dr. Passini at Crossroads Healing Arts, and she gave me seven shots in the painful muscles to relax them. She ordered an MRI and referred me to a Neurosurgeon, getting me in immediately. He examined the MRI and said it was not a neck issue and referred me to a neurologist. The neurologist introduced me to an interesting test, an electromyography (EMG). He placed needles in my shoulder, arm, and hand and then ran electric currents between the needles. It was doable, but not particularly fun. He then made the diagnosis and said it would be a year before the nerve damage would heal in my arm and the numbness and weakness leave my hand. He was accurate in his diagnosis, but once again, had no answer as to why this had happened.

Since my arm was weakened, work on the farm became difficult. One day when using a hammer it kept flying out of my hand. I couldn't figure out why and then remembered that my arm and hand were weakened by the Brachial Plexitis. I also did not have the strength to pull back my bow so there was no archery hunting that fall. Some may not understand, but for me this was a major disappointment. I love the solitude and challenge of archery hunting. During the archery season the woods are quiet and beautiful. There is a peacefulness in wildlife, and I just enjoy being in nature.

To add insult to injury, that fall I was so anxious to get out to the woods that one evening I just went out and sat on my tree stand to see if anything would come by. Before dark the biggest buck I have ever seen in all of my years of hunting whitetail grazed for about 30 minutes right in front of me. I enjoyed watching him. He was a magnificent creature, but of course, I felt helpless just sitting there. Perhaps only hunters will be able to feel my pain, but others can probably imagine how much it hurt to stand witness to my own failing in such a direct way. I whispered to myself, just come back next Saturday when I have a gun, please. As would be expected, I never saw that buck again. I would tell people I could at least go gun hunting, but the truth was my trigger finger was numb and shooting was difficult. After a year, thankfully, my arm was back to normal.

There are many aspects of experiencing illnesses that strip a person of a sense of control. It is easy in these moments to want to give up and stop fighting for better health. The doctors, nurses, and support staff at Crossroads Healing Arts, my primary health care clinic, restored my sense of self at key points in my journey.

This clinic practices integrative health. One of the differences I experienced from my earlier medical doctor is their desire to partner with the patient. They take more time to listen and respect the choices that a patient makes for treatment. When I needed expert medical care for my severe shoulder nerve pain and for my irregular slow heart, they were aggressive in finding me this care. When I chose to consult with an out-of-state endocrinologist in Florida and an internationally-known Lyme specialist in Washington D.C., they were supportive and always remained part of my team. They weren't offended by our decision to reach out to other doctors, but gave us any support we needed. At times, I asked for a lot of specialized care, especially when I would ask them, among other things, to order certain tests and give IV therapies recommended by two specialists I would eventually see, Dr. Lee and Dr. Jemsek. Thankfully, Crossroads Healing Arts continues to be my primary care clinic.

I experienced many positive encounters with medical professionals through my journey towards health. I found emergency room doctors and nurses to be vigilant and kind. During the emergency room visit for the pain in my shoulder they'd discovered that I had large gall bladder stones. As a result, in December of 2009, I had surgery to remove my gall bladder. The surgery was easy and I was home in a few hours. My favorite surgeon, my cousin, Dr. Daniel Diener did the surgery. He asked permission to see if the Nissen surgery I had done years earlier was still in place. When I asked him later what he saw, he said he looked north and all he could see was scar tissue and he looked south and all he could see was scar tissue, so he just closed me up. I enjoyed this kind of candid conversation with doctors. This was the fourth surgery that I had in 2009. Later I would learn that most chronic Lyme patients have had their gallbladder removed.

During this time, Dr. Passini was continually doing blood draws, as many of my blood counts were off. I clearly remember one visit when after reading the results she slammed her hand on the table in frustration and said, "I have tried everything I know and for some reason we cannot lower the C – Reactive Protein (CRP)-count. You have a high level of blood inflammation that I can't seem to help. I have tried everything I know and it just doesn't improve."

CRP is a substance produced by the liver when there is a high level of inflammation in the body. The inflammation can come from a variety of sources and is hard to diagnose. People with a high CRP are at higher risk for heart disease, strokes, and other complications. Basically, it places the entire body at risk. This was one more mysterious problem which seemed to have no answers. I was disheartened.

Later that same month the blood test revealed an elevated homocysteine level. This too is a marker for inflammation somewhere in the body. Homocysteine is an amino acid, one of the building blocks for protein. An elevated homocysteine level increases the risk of heart disease, strokes, and blood clots. As with CRP there are a number of factors that can cause it to be elevated and the cause is difficult to diagnose. This is another example of why it is so difficult to diagnosis Lyme disease. Unless a specialist is able to look at the total picture of one's health history it is impossible to put all the pieces together.

During this time period, another blood test revealed a hyperbilirubinemia. This simply gives evidence that the liver is not functioning properly. Later, during Lyme disease treatment the reason for this became clear; I had an enlarged liver from one of the co-infections that often goes with Lyme disease. Every time I would have an examination during treatment my liver was checked and, fortunately, with treatment it began to decrease in size.

Lyme bacteria love to infiltrate any soft tissue, so it was not only in my liver but also my brain. In the brain, it affects the entire nervous system, and these effects were the most difficult to deal with on a daily basis. One result was numbness in my feet. For about seven years my feet were numb with severe nerve pain every day. Nerve pain is a deep burning sensation that makes you want to scratch, and the more you scratch the more it hurts. These episodes would last for more than a few minutes and would come a few times each day. The numbness made shoes uncomfortable, so when I was in the office alone I would always remove my shoes. I also had pain in the center of the balls of my feet. It would feel like I was walking on a marble, only nothing was there.

In May of 2012 I went back to the neurologist to see if I could get a diagnosis for the numbness. Once again I got the privilege of needles and shock. This time the needles were in my legs and feet. He also tested me by poking the needles into my toes. When he did that I could not feel a thing. He would poke and poke, and then have to poke my leg for a response to make sure I was still awake. He said I have a severe case of neuropathy, but that he didn't know why. I asked him for solutions, and he ordered pain medication. I never took the medication as I knew this was an ongoing issue and did not want to take the medication long term.

Lyme can also affect one's emotions, and I lived with a deep-seated rage within me. It was a constant battle to contain, and particularly devastating because I honestly believe it isn't natural for me to have those intense thoughts and feelings. I would pray for the rage to go away, but it just had become a part of who I was, and something I had to manage. Managing inner rage is not easy during the ups and downs of everyday life. I know my children could see when I was in the moments of dealing with rage. They could see it in my eyes when I was irritable. Julie was especially sensitive to this and knew when to give me space. I hate to admit it, but I also had to be diligent when driving to keep control over my road rage. Any little thing could really tick me off, and I had to constantly manage it.

I have come to believe that the emotional effects of the Lyme bacteria are often more difficult to deal with than the physical. First, there is this never-ending frustration of weakness and lack of answers. It caused me to question my emotional stability and wonder if I was just becoming lazy, a trait opposite of anything I knew about myself. I lived in constant awareness that my rage was unpredictable and there were times when I lived with regret of saying too much. I know how much damage words can do, so I was constantly on guard. It is hard to describe what it is like to live with rage that one does not understand, and to be afraid that it would become manifest in a very unhealthy way.

---

from Julie:

It wasn't until sometime during Terry's treatment for Lyme disease, that I began to understand what Terry explained as rage. It is not a term I would have placed on his sometimes irritability and tenseness for years. Even though I have to believe that Terry felt the inner rage most of the time. It must have taken an incredible amount of energy for him to disguise and "manage" his feelings he calls rage.

I always believed that he became tense and irritable due to his constant fatigue and all of the unknown health issues he was having. And yes, I learned how to give him space and rest. His emotions were no surprise to me as I have spent years working with persons who are ill, and his did not seem out of the ordinary. What we as a family experienced did not seem as rage. As I wrote in another place, Terry suffered quietly and rarely even complained to me.

Terry admits to desperately hiding his emotions from me, which he did. During his first visit with the Lyme specialist, we soon understood that rage was a common symptom of this disease. When the nervous system is under attack, it affects many aspects of someone's life. I know I cannot truly know what he was experiencing.

When I think of all that our family experienced during the twelve years of his undiagnosed illness, I am amazed. All three of our children graduated from high school, then all three attended college which meant moving furniture here and there. Our youngest son, Casey, spent a year in Thailand where we went to visit him. Terry officiated our daughter Lindsy's wedding to Joe Locke in 2010 along with numerous nieces and nephews on both sides of our family. It seems as if Terry should have exploded with rage while working many long hours for the church and having a hectic family life as well!

More Than Tired

B y now I was living with even more extreme fatigue. I would wake up in the morning and simply not want to get out of bed. I wondered how a person could feel so tired after sleeping all night. My body would feel heavy, and all it wanted to do was to remain lying down. I would force myself to get up and go to work, but by midafternoon I would hit the wall and often go home and sleep. This was especially necessary if I had evening meetings. Again, I felt that if I pushed myself I could keep going and function, but as soon as I got home, I would sit in my recliner and go into a deep rest.

People began to comment that I looked tired. A number of times when I would go through the drive-thru at a fast food restaurant the person serving me would say, "You look really tired. Are you doing okay?" I wondered how many other people they would say that to. One Sunday morning I climbed the long, steep steps from our sanctuary to the balcony to meet with the people in the technology booth. When I arrived at the booth the PowerPoint person said, "A person your age should not look like you just did walking up those steps. You looked like it took a real effort." I just smiled and thought, you have no idea how tired I feel and how exhausting it was to make it up those steps.

During this time, I also developed continual headaches. I would go to sleep with a headache and wake up with it. The ache shot across my forehead and the top of my head. It wasn't severe but always there. I can only describe it as a pressure headache. Tylenol made no difference. The greatest pain and pressure was behind my right eye which had had the retinal bleed a few years earlier. This eye would tend to bulge when it was at its worse. Others would not notice but Julie always could see it, and she would claim the eye looked glassy and that the small veins in my right temple would bulge.

During one of many blood draws at Crossroad Healing Arts in June of 2011, the nurse noticed that my heart rate was irregular and slow. I was essentially missing every other beat and the rate was in the low 40s. I was immediately taken to an examination room and Dr. Passini examined me. This was a scary experience as it was the first time I had heart issues. She determined that it was not a crisis and referred me to a cardiologist who did the routine cardiac work-up and tried some medication to correct the heart rate. Both Julie and I were really concerned as it seemed my health issues were only getting worse.

A week or two later I had a follow-up EKG, and within hours the doctor called and told me to immediately stop the medication as it made my heart even more erratic. It was a relief to have that answer as to how I was feeling. He referred me to an electro physiologist for further evaluation. We made this appointment as quickly as possible. When dealing with heart-related issues time is of essence.

Several weeks later I had my first heart ablation which was not successful. He believed the unwanted electrical impulses were coming from the center area of my heart. He had done some treating of the area, but did not want to proceed without talking with me. Moving forward was risky because of the area of the heart it involved. He said if he aggressively treated that area and was not successful he could in essence stop my heart and then be forced to install a pacemaker. I would be 100% dependent on a pacemaker which meant that if something went wrong with the pacemaker, I would die immediately.

This was the most unsettling part of my journey to this point. I knew that I would not have any quality of life if we just let it go, but Julie and I were not ready to allow the procedure as it had been explained to us.

My heart rate was even slower after the ablation, so not only was I having much fatigue from the Lyme, but now my heart wasn't functioning properly. I was becoming winded and struggled with any amount of physical work or exertion. I clearly remember one afternoon when I was building a platform to place a tree stand on, and after digging four holes for the posts I laid the shovel down and sat under a shade tree. I simply had to rest and leave my project partly finished. I did not have the physical stamina to do what I considered to be a simple task.

Julie quickly resolved that we would go to Cleveland Clinic for a second opinion, and we refused to schedule a second ablation. We were not comfortable about my becoming dependent on a pacemaker, but also knew that if nothing was done, the heart issue was going to permanently change me and our quality of life. It was at this time in my journey of random health crises, one weird crisis after another, that we realized how seriously ill I was becoming. We were both shook and worried. Whatever my underlying illness was, it was wreaking havoc inside my body and throughout our life. Of course, at this point we still had no idea that it was chronic Lyme disease.

Heart

We called Cleveland Clinic, an amazing hospital that makes a commitment to see any heart patient within 24 hours of their first call. When we got there we met Dr. Tarakji. This was January 2012. I had a conversation with the nurse who admitted me that stands out as a restorative moment in a time of great uncertainty. Unlike so many conversations where my sense of self faded into the background, this one made me feel recognized for a real part of who I am.

When I told her that I was a pastor she said her mother was a pastor as well. She asked about the size of my church and replied, "You are the shepherd of a small village. We have to get you fixed up. Your church people need you and you cannot function with your heart the way it is now. I am going to tell the doctor he needs to fix you quick." And as Dr. Tarakji entered and she was leaving, she did just that: "Doctor, this patient's church needs him and he needs your help." I just smiled and appreciated her care and energy.

I met with Tarakji who was very intense and asked probing questions. I had come to appreciate doctors like this who spend a lot of time and asked tough questions. He asked if I had any idea what my quality of life would be if I was living by the power of a pacemaker? He really tried to understand and cared deeply about my sense of things. After he was satisfied with his knowledge of my situation, he agreed to set a time for the following week to have the ablation. I was relieved to have another ablation scheduled, and gained confidence from the fact that he performs this procedure several times a week and has many colleagues to consult.

We had another consult with him the day before the surgery, and he had more questions and more advice. We were startled to learn that he had decided he was not comfortable doing the procedure. According to the report of the earlier ablation, he believed the problem would likely be in the core area of the heart. He told us he would not enter that area. He would not do anything that could lead to a pacemaker. He was clear that I did not want that, and he would not place one in. I was too young for a pacemaker, he was certain. Actually, he was trying to talk me out of doing the entire procedure. Finally, I told him that I understood his caution and appreciated that he did not want to take any chances. But I asked if there was a possibility that he could even go into the heart and just look around as a second opinion. Somehow I communicated my persistence and desperation, and he took heart.

After more discussion, he finally agreed to go in and look around, but then we were shocked by what he said next. He told us he may do a more drastic move and go through the septum, the wall between the right and left atriums, to explore the left atrium. We were told that it makes the procedure much riskier, but if he is going in, he needed our consent to do that if necessary. We agreed. After all, we had hundreds of people back in Indiana praying for us and for the outcome of this procedure.

The next morning the ablation started early. An ablation is a procedure where they run wires through the groin and up into the heart. During the procedure you are awake and have to lay on your back completely still. At one point when my leg muscle was tightening up I rotated my foot a bit. He said," Mr. Diener you cannot move." I knew this was going to be a long six hours.

He went into the right upper chamber of my heart and found nothing. He then sent the needle through the dividing wall of my heart into the left chamber. All of a sudden he shouted, "I found it!" and in a matter of a couple of minutes there were six doctors around me viewing the monitor. Everyone was excited by what he discovered. He burned the area, and instantly my heart rate returned to normal. The risk was worth it.

I then had to lay for another hour while two nurses applied pressure to stop the bleeding in the area where they had sent in the wires. From there I went to my room and lay on my back for another three hours. When I got up to go to the bathroom I left a trail of spots of blood on the floor. The nurse said, "Sorry, but you need three more hours on your back and then we will try again." It was a long day, but worth it.

As was usually the case, there were special people in my life who waited the hours while I was in surgery. As pastor, I have waited with people for many surgeries and know those can be long days for the support people as well. Lindsy, my brother Ron, pastor Danny Yoder, and a friend waited with Julie to hear the doctor's report, and of course were overjoyed when told the good news. This was the kind of support I had learned to expect.

At our follow-up visit I asked Dr. Tarakji if this could happen again. He said anything is possible but there is no reason it should. When I asked why it happened in the first place, he simply said I don't have any good answer for that. By this time I was getting used to that response. Just one more crazy abnormal health issue on my list. It seemed like when it came to weird health issues I was particularly blessed. We would later learn that many persons with Lyme have heart issues as the bacteria burrows into the soft heart tissue.

Dr. Tarakji referred me to an endocrinologist at Cleveland Clinic for further evaluation. She did an extensive blood work up and all the results came back normal. The main thing she was interested in was the function of my adrenals, and she said they were working well. She ordered an MRI to check out my pituitary gland. Since it was an MRI of my head, my head was confined in something that looks like a baseball catcher's mask. It grasped the head tightly which made a person like me who has minor claustrophobia feel even more confined. The MRI revealed an empty sella which meant my pituitary gland was concave in the front. The pituitary gland is critical as it controls the whole endocrine system, especially the thyroid and adrenals. I questioned her report that all my blood results were good, but I never knew for sure as she canceled my follow-up appointment due to her unexpected move back to Turkey.

At least my heart was beating on its own.

------

from Julie:

When it became obvious that Terry's doctor at Cleveland clinic did not want to do an ablation at all, but wanted Terry to learn to live with his disabled heart, I was so dumbfounded. I couldn't speak at all. Terry was somehow able to continue the conversation. After our appointment, we sat in the motel room quietly, unable to eat and barely talking. We were both shocked, fearful, and questioning our own judgment. We wondered was God trying to tell us something? I believe that neither one of us slept much if at all that night. By morning I felt at peace about moving forward. Our daughter Lindsy took a day off work and drove out in the wee hours of the morning. Pastor Danny, a friend, and Terry's brother Ron were also there with me during the long hours of the procedure. The finding and repair of his heart irregularity was truly a miracle, with the outcome way exceeding our hopes. Dr. Tarakji 's comments following the procedure reflected great surprise and disbelief in the location of the problem he found in the left atrium. Treatment to the area was simple and to this day Terry's heart rate has been perfectly regular. What a miracle!

Rest and Hope

One of the difficult parts of an illness journey is knowing what to say to friends and the church, and when to talk about my health issues. The church, especially its leaders, had a right to know since my health affects my work performance. At the same time, I did not want to worry them with unnecessary details. People at church kept asking, and I knew they wanted an honest response, but so often I just did not know what to say.

At this point the cards and notes of encouragement started flowing my way. I always felt tremendous support and knew they did not blame me for how things were and just genuinely cared for me. All of the cards included expressions such as, "We are praying for you." I had the special blessing of a "prayer shield" through all these years of pastoring and health issues. Three special men in my life, Aldine Thomas, Lydell Troyer, and Pete Bontrager, met with me monthly for prayer. I could share with them anything that was on my heart, from church to family to health. Those prayer times were so special. Aldine passed away in the winter of 2015, but Lydell and Pete continued to meet with me.

Dr. Passini had left Crossroad Healing Arts so I began to see Dr. Anderson. Dr. Anderson was also a doctor who listened well and was constantly seeking answers for me. One afternoon when reviewing my latest blood work and my lengthy health chart he said we had to have a heart-to-heart conversation. He told me I needed to take a six-week medical leave beginning immediately. He didn't know what was wrong, but I had to do something to change the direction my health was going. Since Julie was in the room and heard what he said, I knew that I had no choice.

That night I told the congregational oversight board about the doctor's order for a six-week medical leave, and they immediately said I must do it. I am thankful for the constant care and support I received from the Board. They put my health first, even when it was hard for me to do so. I wondered if it was right for a pastor to place his own health before the needs of the congregation. Putting my needs first was something I struggled with greatly. At the same time, I knew my health was failing and had no idea why. I also knew that if something didn't change I would not be pastoring much longer anyway. Because of a crisis in the church I could not take my leave until three weeks later, but right after that I began my six-week leave.

A passage of Scripture that became a source of strength during these months is Isaiah 43: 1- 4, New Living Translation with some personal translation: *Listen to the Lord who created you, the one who formed you. Do not be afraid, for I have redeemed you, I have called you by name, you are mine. When you go through deep waters, I will be with you. When you go through rivers of difficulty, you will not drown (you will not be overwhelmed). When you walk through the fire of oppression, you will not be burned up; the flames will not consume you. For I am the Lord, your God, the Holy One of Israel, your Savior. Because you are precious in my sight. You are honored, and I love you.*

I love this passage for so many reasons. First of all, the intimate knowledge God has of me as my creator. While my health was a mystery to myself and doctors, God was fully aware of what was happening in my body. He knows my name, that is how important I am to him. I belong to him. And finally, he walks with me. I have always believed that God has never promised that this life would be a piece of cake. He never promised that life would always be easy, but he promises to walk with us. When we enter the valley, He goes before and behind and is all around us. I especially found strength from the line about not drowning which really means not to be overwhelmed.

When I allowed myself to focus on my health issues it was easy to feel overwhelmed. There was so much uncertainty and no clear answers. All I knew was that my health was failing, and in Isaiah there is a promise that I will not be overwhelmed because God walks with me. And finally, the last line, where once again God's love and care for me is expressed. In God's sight I am precious, honored, and loved. What more can a person ask for?

This passage sustained me at this point in my journey and would sustain me in the years ahead. It is a passage that I have shared with many persons who are struggling with real life issues that cause pain. I hope it brings them the comfort and strength it has given to me.

When we began the medical leave Julie and I immediately flew to our favorite place in Colorado to try to relax. She was reading a book, *Live Well, Feel Younger* by Dr. Edwin Lee, an ironic title for how I was feeling. A nurse at Crossroad Healing Arts had given it to Julie, telling her that she had read it and could see me all over it. As Julie read it, she too kept saying that the author was describing me. She wanted me to read it as well, which I resisted. At this point I was tired of trying to find answers. I was beginning to resolve in myself that I would never get better. Besides, I was still wondering if it all was just in my head.

She began to say that we are going to make an appointment with Dr.

Lee and see if he might have some answers. I said, "No way does a person in northern Indiana go to Orlando, Florida to see a doctor." She was convinced that we would go any distance required for help, and when I read the book I had to admit that maybe he could be helpful. It was Monday of Labor Day Weekend 2011. I told her that she could call Dr. Lee's office and if they could see me in two weeks, during my medical leave, I would go. I would not go if I had to wait two months. I was expecting the latter.

Indiana to Florida

Tuesday morning Julie called Dr. Lee's clinic, and the receptionist said she had just gotten off the phone with someone who had cancelled. If we could be there Thursday at 9:00 a.m., we could have the appointment. I believe that God was at work, and if God wasn't, then Julie certainly was. I knew we were on our way to Florida.

We got tickets to fly home from Colorado yet that afternoon and then to Florida on Wednesday. Julie has a way of getting things done when she is on a mission. We flew home, got the large file of my medical records, and Thursday morning at 8:30 were sitting in Dr. Lee's office anxious to see him.

At 9:00 we were sent to a room that was like a living room, spacious and with couches. We were given tea to drink and then Dr. Lee came in. The first thing I said after the formal greeting was, "You are the last doctor I am going to see. I have seen many doctors over the past years, and I will not see one more. I hope you can help me because you are my last chance." He smiled and said we will see about that. I don't think he knew that I was serious. By this point in the journey I was so tired of spending my life in doctor offices and taking medical tests. I was just weary.

For over two hours we sat and chatted. I had never experienced such a doctor. He asked probing questions, but then would sit quietly and listen giving me space to think and respond. He didn't take over the conversation but waited for me to continue when I paused, which I didn't do very much. I poured out my whole health story, and by the end of the appointment I had a sense that he had heard me and understood. He accepted and believed that there was something major going on with my health and that it came from one main source that had not yet been discovered. It is healing to be listened to and believed.

He told me I had to work at my overall health which included losing some weight. He also said I had drank my last diet coke. Earlier, when he had asked if I drink diet coke, I'd downplayed the amount and said about eight cans a day. Really, it was much more. With my fatigue I was desperate for caffeine, even though caffeine did not help much. In the morning when I woke up I had a diet coke, and I had one again before I went to bed. How many I had between I didn't count. I just drank diet coke throughout the day.

He told us to go have lunch and that we would meet in the afternoon to discuss a treatment plan. He suggested a restaurant, and I thought for lunch I would have my "last diet coke." When I ordered my meal I was told they do not have sodas. When we met with Dr. Lee in the afternoon I said the restaurant did not have diet coke. He replied," I know, that is why I recommended it."

Dr. Lee was mostly concerned about my adrenal function and said blood tests are not effective in diagnosing adrenals. He ordered a saliva test and prescribed a number of supplements and pills to boost my immune system. He was also concerned about my thyroid and ordered an ultrasound. He was interested in my empty sella and asked when I had suffered a head injury. I told him I never experienced a head injury which surprised him as he said that is really the only thing that can cause an empty sella. One more mystery of something that was wrong and had no explanation.

Dr. Lee's main line of attack was detox and liver cleanse. He ordered a detox IV which I took in his clinic before I left. This was a detox IV I would continue to do weekly at Crossroad Healings Arts. He ordered a detox program that involved taking his shakes and eating only Brussel sprouts, cauliflower, cabbage, and broccoli for ten days. I did this regiment two times. He also wanted me to use my dry heat sauna several times a week, and he gave me detox pills to take. His emphasis was building up my immune system and lowering inflammation in my body. Following his instructions added greatly to the amount of time now focused toward healing, but at least I had a new-found hope of getting better.

When we got home I had an ultrasound of my thyroid which revealed multiple nodules. Dr. Lee then ordered a needle biopsy to check for cancer. The first biopsy came back inconclusive which is a common result for this test. I did it again and this time they were much more aggressive. It hurt a bit more, but they got a good sample and it came back benign. I was relieved since I had been told that at least one nodule was suspicious. However, since my thyroid function was down, Dr. Lee ordered medicine to make up for what my thyroid was not producing.

I did the saliva test which showed I was in severe adrenal fatigue. It had not yet reached the point of adrenal crises which was a praise as once it reaches that point the adrenals are gone and will not come back. Dr. Lee was fairly confident that with aggressive treatment my adrenals could be saved. Adrenal fatigue was a major reason for my severe lack of energy, a major player in that wall I would hit. Adrenals are supposed to replenish themselves during the night and mine did not. This was why I woke up each morning feeling tired. Dr. Lee prescribed a high level of hydrocortisone. Healthy adrenals produce cortisone, and obviously my adrenals were not. When we checked out, the discharge nurse told us that I must really be in bad shape as Dr. Lee hardly ever prescribes hydrocortisone and certainly not this amount. I knew Dr. Lee was trying to jump start my system.

Dr. Lee also ordered me to do a sleep study to test for sleep apnea. I took the test at the Goshen Sleep Center and failed, so I got to begin to sleep with a CPAP machine. Sleeping with a mask tight to my face connected to a hose is not the greatest, but it does help me have a deeper sleep.

With the advantage of hindsight, we now know that the Lyme had infiltrated the sleep center of my brain which had a negative impact on my sleep patterns. One of the results of this was horrible nightmares. Every night someone would try to kill me. All night I would be on the run. The dreams were vivid and in the morning I would remember every detail. When being examined for Lyme disease I was asked if I was an observer or active participant in my dreams. I assured her that I was an active participant.

In one nightmare, I was being forced to walk across a huge canyon on a tight wire. There were two guys with guns making me do this. If I were to reach the other side I could go free. About halfway across the canyon I began to fall and reached for a vine. At that part of the nightmare I grabbed the hose of my machine and jerked it, sending the machine rolling across the floor. Both Julie and I sat straight up in bed at the racket. We both had a good laugh before I recovered my machine and tried to go back to sleep. I am thankful Julie will sleep with me, not surprised but grateful. This is her journey too.

A month later we had a follow-up appointment with Dr. Lee. Julie and I took the opportunity to spend a week in Florida and invited my sister, Marlene, and her husband, Gary, along with another couple to join us. We had a wonderful few days in Florida relaxing on the beach, playing cards, and enjoying great conversation. The vacation and medical leave ended abruptly due to a tragedy in one of the families in our church. I knew I needed to return immediately to walk with the family and church through this crisis. So my medical leave ended a week early, but it had been a wonderful gift from the congregation, a time of rest and most importantly, I had met Dr. Lee and was now under his care.

The Long Haul

During my medical leave, I read the book *Courageous Leader* by Bill Hybels. It was an inspirational and challenging book as I reflected on my pastoral ministry and calling, but one chapter especially connected. *"Enduring Spirit"* begins with Hybel's reflections on his interviews with five highly effective pastors he was mentoring. He asked each of them about the most pressing questions they faced and their responses surprised him.

One said, "How am I going to find the strength to keep going?" Another asked, "Is my life in ministry sustainable over the long haul?" and finally one somewhat truthfully joked, "How can I time my burn out just before my crack up?" Hybel went on to say that many pastors live with a sense that they cannot maintain over the long haul the level of activity and stress they experience. The most burning feeling for each of them was a deep sense that they would not survive their calling or live to cross the finish line.

I realize that many pastors carry the sense that they cannot sustain the pace of their ministerial life long-term, but reasons for that feeling vary.

I know now that I was living with health issues that had not yet been discovered, but in the years before my medical leave I too had a deep sense I could not keep up the pace and demands of pastoral ministry for much longer. This was one of the main reasons I was willing to take a medical leave when it was recommended. While I felt selfish to put my own needs ahead of the needs of the congregation, I was fully aware that if I didn't find a solution to my health that I would not be around for the long haul anyway.

The year after beginning care with Dr. Lee, I continued to improve slowly, but at the same time there were additional concerns. My adrenals were not coming back, and Dr. Lee continued to be suspicious of my thyroid and ordered another needle biopsy. This one also came back negative, so cancer was firmly ruled out. During this time, Dr. Anderson wanted me to do a test called a thermogram that would highlight the areas of pain in my body. When we went over the test results it showed high levels of pain in my shoulders and back, but I did not feel it was as severe as the test concluded. I'd had chronic continuous pain and muscle tightness in my shoulders for years. There had been a large lump, which I felt was a bundle of nerves on top of my left shoulder that I would often rub and ask Julie to rub. I had many massages but nothing seemed to really provide relief.

My lower back was also sore, and I had just assumed that at some point I would probably need back surgery since my father and brother had both had it. I asked Dr. Anderson if one diagnosis for this kind of pain could be Fibromyalgia. He said it could be diagnosed that way, but wasn't sure it fit for me. I later learned that Fibromyalgia is often a diagnosis for persons with Lyme. After my treatment for Lyme all of that pain was gone. Even the large lump on my shoulder disappeared. Only when it was gone did I realized how much pain I had lived with over the years.

It was during these years 2011–2012 that Julie, based upon her research, became very suspicious of Lyme disease. She was tireless in trying to find the ultimate solution to my health issues. We talked with Dr. Lee about this, and he was open to doing testing to see if Lyme was behind all of these health problems. He was a bit frustrated that I was not improving in the way he had thought I would and considered Lyme a possibility. He wanted us to use IGenx laboratories as it was the "gold standard" lab for infectious disease. Dr. Anderson was willing to order the IGenx lab, but first he had to order a standard Lyme test, the ELISA through our local hospital. He said he was sure it would come back negative, but it was a necessary first step in the process.

The test was negative, of course. Testing for Lyme, we would learn, is flawed and essentially invalid. The medical world only accepts the ELISA/Western Blot testing which even the Center for Disease Control (CDC) says has only 50% accuracy. The CDC does go on to say that diagnosis of Lyme cannot be made by testing alone, but by symptoms. However, the cases of hundreds of thousands of patients show that medical doctors will only look at testing. So we proceeded to draw blood and pay out-of-pocket for the IGenx test for Lyme.

Results from the IGenx lab were complicated, and we could not figure out how to read them. When we first looked at it we thought the result was negative, but that was according to the CDC. Then, it seems, God intervened again.

Julie had a conversation with her cousin, Renette, who lived in the Washington D.C. area. Their family had walked the Lyme journey with their daughter, Stephanie. Renette understood the language of the test and said that according to the lab result, Lyme borreliosis was definitely positive. The CDC accepts only lab tests that have been approved by the Food and Drug Administration (FDA), even though the testing IGenx labs does for Lyme has 93% accuracy. IGenx, along with other labs with more accurate forms of testing, have been approved by all of the regulatory testing except for FDA. This is just one of many ways the medical establishment controls the diagnosis of Lyme. When Renette heard only a bit of my health issues she said she was sure that Lyme was the underlying cause of all I had been through.

Renette's daughter, Stephanie, became very ill at age 11 with seizures, body pain, and other health issues, essentially becoming debilitated and unable to attend school. Like tens of thousands of other chronic Lyme patients, they had no answers after visits to many doctors. As a last resort she spent a week at Mayo clinic for rigorous testing, but they sent her home saying she is very sick, but they just could not determine why. When they finally had the IGenx testing for Lyme, and pursued treatment, they chose to be treated in North Carolina by a Lyme-literate specialist, Dr. Joseph Jemsek.

They lived in Washington D.C., but out of desperation made the many trips required to Dr. Jemsek's North Carolina clinic to receive treatment. Stephanie's treatment lasted several years, but she is now well enough to attend college. Julie was convinced, and I was too, that we needed to pursue treatment for Lyme, and it was through Renette's experience and guidance that we ultimately chose the same physician, although now he was thankfully practicing in Washington, D.C.

Renette has been and continues to be active as an advocate for those living with Lyme disease, both in the political world and socially as a support to many who are desperately looking for help. One thing she told us was that nearly every person she knows with chronic Lyme no longer has a gallbladder, and most have neuropathy of their feet or legs. How true it was for me. Renette's knowledge and grace are true gifts to us on this journey.

Dr. Jemsek

At our next visit with Dr. Lee, he encouraged us to find a Lyme specialist. I appreciate a doctor who knows his own limitations and is helpful in making referrals to other specialists. He recommended two, one in Seattle and Dr. Jemsek in Washington D.C. He preferred I go to the one in Seattle since his treatment was more natural and Dr. Jemsek's was more medically-oriented, but he supported us choosing either of them. I told him that a person in Indiana does not go as far as Seattle to see a doctor. His reply was that it is not too far if I want to get well. His strict counsel was that we had to go to a Lyme specialist. To get the best care, we had to go to someone who worked exclusively with Lyme patients.

After reading more about the protocols of both doctors, I chose Dr. Jemsek. The more natural approach would take at least two years of treatment with possible need for antibiotics after the treatment. And it would have basically required us to move to Seattle to do the treatment.

We called Dr. Jemsek's office, and the earliest we could get in to see him was in four months. Fortunately, we could be on a waiting list if we were willing to go on a short notice. We were willing to drop anything if they called. A couple of weeks later they called and said there was an opening in one month. We said we'd be there. This worked out perfectly since I was officiating at my niece's wedding in Virginia on Saturday, October 27th and the appointment was the Monday morning following, October 29, 2012.

After the wedding and a wonderful time with family we left for D.C. on Sunday afternoon. The weather bulletins said Hurricane Sandy was to hit the east coast late Sunday night and we wondered if the clinic would be open. But nothing was going to stop us now, not even a hurricane, so we drove into D.C.

We stopped at a pharmacy and bought two umbrellas. All the public schools and public transportation were already closed because of the hurricane, and we really expected the clinic to be closed. Fortunately, our hotel was only a two-block walk from the clinic so we decided we might as well show up and see. The next morning, we woke up to high winds and pouring rain. The hurricane had arrived, but the eye of the storm was going further north so D.C. would not get the worst of the storm. We got out the umbrellas and with an accordion file full of my health history we walked to the clinic. By God's grace it was open. We were so excited to get our appointment started.

Dr. Jemsek is a doctor who has dedicated his life to the research and treatment of infectious diseases. During the 1980s in his work with HIV he saw thousands of patients, most of them young and dying from this incurable disease. Being a compassionate, humble, and dedicated doctor, all of his energy and expertise was given in developing a solution to HIV/AIDS. While seeing thousands of patients, he became one of the major players and pioneers in the development of treatment for HIV. Dr. Jemsek has received many awards for his work in the field of HIV/AIDS. In 1998, he received the Governor's Award—Certificate of Appreciation—presented by Governor James Hunt of North Carolina.

In 2004, as part of Governor's World Aids Day, he was presented with the Volunteer Service Award. He was interviewed on *60 minutes, 20\20,* and *Good Morning America.*

In 2001, he began to see many patients with an illness possibly attributed to Lyme Borreliosis. Dr. Jemsek has said that it took about a year to appreciate and accept the validity of the disease. At that time, he was still involved with HIV/AIDS medicine, but his reputation as a listening and caring physician was out there, and more and more persons suffering from chronic Lyme disease sought him out.

Dr. Jemsek in a statement to the State Medical Board of North Carolina has said the following:

Most of my HIV patients used to die, now most don't. Some still do of course. My Lyme patients, the sickest ones, want to die but they can't. That's right, they want to die but they can't. The most common cause of death in Lyme disease is suicide. Patients suffering with advanced Lyme Borreliosis Complex have an inferior quality of life compared to those with HIV/AIDS.

In time, Dr. Jemsek focused fully on walking with patients of Lyme disease, and he is greatly involved in research for finding better systems for diagnosing and treating Lyme patients. Although the medical establishment stands against him and insurance companies will not cover his service, he relentlessly seeks to provide compassionate expert care to Lyme sufferers who are desperate for answers. He is quoted as having said,

When patients come to see us, the sick folks have usually been seen by up to ten to twenty doctors and have often been referred to major medical centers, ranging from Mayo to Cleveland Clinic, Duke and others. They have had numerous tests, trials of therapy, and are often left with labels such as depression, fibromyalgia, chronic fatigue, MS, and more. They're not happy because they've spent up to or exceeding $150,000 and they are suffering and/or dysfunctional.

As it was for me, Dr. Jemsek is seen as being their last hope. And hope and healing is what this amazing doctor offers. In a four-year period, he treated over 900 new patients each year. He is one of the leaders in the fight against this horrible disease. I am grateful that I was referred to him, and from my first visit in his clinic I had hope.

Hope

The first morning at the Jemsek Clinic we met with a physician assistant, Kim Fogarty. She is an energetic, fun person who can do a very thorough examination. Her positive attitude and contagious smile helped make the poking and prodding and many different exercises almost fun. We spent about three hours with her answering questions that I knew were revealing my health struggles. It is amazing how discussing my frustrating and painful journey brought healing when shared with someone who was so attentive. We immediately liked and trusted her.

She read over the huge medical file that Julie always took to an appointment and then said she would need some time to make a determination. She was gone about a half hour. When she returned, she said, "Mr. Diener, I am 100% sure that you have Lyme disease and that we can help you."

The tears began to flow down my cheeks as they are doing now as I remember that powerful moment. At last I had a firm diagnosis with the promise, "we can help you." Honestly, before that statement I questioned if I really had Lyme, and I certainly doubted if there was really a successful treatment for me. It was so emotional to hear those words: "Mr. Diener, I am 100% sure you have Lyme disease and that we can help you." There is no way I can express how wonderful it was when what I had been feeling and dealing with for years was finally validated. We had been searching for answers for twelve years.

Empty sella is one example of the difficulty of diagnosing Lyme and the horrific effects it can have on one's body. Kim earmarked empty sella, a concave pituitary gland, as one indicator of Lyme disease. Rare in the general population, empty sella was common in her patients, all of whom have Lyme disease. Looking for something I could cite to others as proof of my condition, I asked if there is a test that could establish the correlation between empty sella and Lyme disease. She said there wasn't. So many symptoms have no clear medical explanation. Bacteria quietly and persistently do their damage, attacking the pituitary gland, thyroid, adrenals, and any other soft tissue in the body. This lack of concrete proof is so damaging to us who suffer without explanation.

We talked more, and then she left to begin to write up a treatment plan. While she was gone, Dr. Jemsek came into our room to visit. We did not expect to meet with him. We had been told that most patients do not meet him until they have been in treatment for a few months, and here we were meeting him on our first visit. I think part of the reason for this was that only a few patients showed up that morning because of the hurricane.

Entering the room, he said, "Good morning, Reverend Diener." He seemed to get a kick out of calling me reverend and intrigued by me being a pastor. He said, "Reverend, you have seen too many doctors and have had too many health crises. You have been bailing water as hard as you can for a long time, and the water is coming in faster than you can bail." I was taken aback. No one had ever given me a better way to describe my health situation over the past years. I was trying hard. It felt like I was doing everything I could do, but it seemed that I was slowly losing ground. He said the good news is we can help you with this and began to give an overview of possible treatment. It sounded time-consuming and pretty brutal, so I asked him what would happen if I don't do the treatment. He replied, "Oh, your ship will sink. There is no way you can keep bailing water forever."

This conversation with Dr. Jemsek was an incredible blessing. It felt like another affirmation that we were on the right path and that God was walking closely with us. Special moments and conversations like these are long remembered and would be vital in sustaining us in the journey ahead.

Kim then returned and went over the treatment plan with us. She explained that she did not want to start treatment until January and at that point was not sure if the treatment would be oral medication or if we would start with IV therapy. It would take a few months to build up my immune system to the point of being able to go through the treatment. She ordered many supplements to boost my immune system and medications to calm my nervous system which was on high alert. There were many examples of my tense nerves. First, there was the neuropathy, but there was also the underlying rage I felt, in part due to stress on my nervous system. Although, I wanted to start treatment immediately, I could see the wisdom of first getting my nervous system under control. We set the date to return and then left at one o'clock.

We are pretty sure I was the only patient seen that day. The staff left right behind us as they all wanted to get home before the storm hit in full force. The walk back to the hotel was through sheets of driving rain, and when we arrived at the hotel we asked the staff to please get our car so we could head home. They cautioned us against leaving because of the storm, but we convinced them that our situation was an exception. There were high winds and pouring rain as we drove through the city, but the good thing was that the roads were almost deserted. Thirty minutes after we left D.C. we heard on the radio that all bridges in and out of the city were being closed. We were glad we were on the road, but drove through the storm until Cleveland, Ohio. The best part of getting home was that we had been given hope that we had not felt for a long time.

Reports

D r. Jemsek prefers the term Lyme Borreliosis Complex (LBC) because
of the multiple coexisting infections that have to be treated. Lyme
borrelia is bacteria that can and will infect any system in the body. Our
understanding is that it loves first and foremost the brain, affecting the
central nervous system, but also any organ or soft tissue in the body.
Whereabouts it inhabits in the brain will determine the symptoms. So
far, we knew I had a severe sleep disorder, and the neuropathy in my
feet and my headaches were certainly from infected areas in the brain.
Symptoms can vary drastically from one person to the next. We were
only beginning to learn the extent to which it is a silent, invisible disease.
The suffering and damage it does is quiet and internal.

Co-infections enter the body alongside the Lyme bacteria. The most
common co-infections are babesia, ehrlichia, and bartonella, and there
are others. Babesia is the co-infection that explains my persistently
enlarged liver and spleen, and from Julie's studies we learned it can be the
most difficult to treat. Co-infections add to the extreme complexity of
the disease and its treatment. The bacteria live in clusters having a heavy

biofilm, or covering to protect itself, and the bacteria mutate quickly and repeatedly in response to treatment.

Within a week of our first visit we received a ten-page report on our consultation written by Jemsek's physician assistant, Kim. I had never before seen such a precise and detailed health history. Reading the report raised my level of trust in her. She had read all of my medical and medication history, listened intently to my experience, and performed an extensive examination. It helped me to see all of my health history in one concise but all-inclusive report. With that perspective, I could understand in a new way all that I had been through. At the same time, it awakened me to the seriousness of my health situation. Even just a bit of her report provides a helpful medical perspective of my journey.

Impression:

1. Lyme borreliosis complex – supporting I GeneX IgM (IND 39, 1 + 41, 1+ 83-93) 05/2012.
   a. Extensive tick exposure throughout lifetime.
   b. Development of atypical progressive fatigue, and unexplained fever 01/2000
   c. Dysomnia – vivid dreams and dystonia upon initiation (limbic)
      (1) Sleep study (11/2011) revealing mixed central sleep apnea and obstructive sleep apnea along with periodic limb movement.
   d. Cognitive dysfunction - brain fog, short-term memory
   e. Mononeuritis multiplex – radicular pain in the lower extremities, numbness in the extremities, cervical plexitis, carotidynia.
      (1) EMG/NCV 2009 revealing right brachial plexitis.
      (2) EMG 05/2012 lower extremities revealing sensory motor neuropathy.
   f. B signs and symptoms – neck and lumbar pain.
      (1) Atraumatic left shoulder labral tear status post repair 2006.

(2) Status post arthroscopic repair right knee (meniscal injury).

g. Fatigue state – marked.

h. Cerebellar dysfunction – by history and examination.

i. Dermatitis – cherry angiomata, cystic lesion right lower lip.

j. Frontal headaches.

k. Limbic irritability – uncharacteristic irritability and anger; photophobia.

l. MRI scan of the brain without contrast 2011 – partial empty sella; mild mucosal thickening of the sinuses; congestion of cerebellar foramen with mild atrophy.

m. HPA dysfunction – hypogonadism, low adrenal insufficiency – followed by endocrinologist Dr. Lee.

2. GI – episodes of alternating diarrhea and constipation; postprandial abdominal cramping with tenesmus.

3. Multinodular goiter with colloid cysts – benign biopsy x2 – patient being managed by endocrinologist Dr. Lee.

4. Status post cardiac ablation x2 – bradycardia and PAC's 06/20/2011 and 01/2012.

a. 02/25/2011 nuclear stress test revealing fixed defect inferolateral wall attributed to attenuation.

b. Transesophageal echocardiogram 03/04/2011 revealing trace mitral regurgitation.

c. Hyperhomocysteinemia.

d. Carotid ultrasound 2011 revealing 50-75% stenosis right external carotid; mild (less than 50%) left external carotid.

5. Right retinal vein occlusion 2008 – suspected to be attributed to by #1 – followed by yearly examinations by retinal specialist.

6. Gastroesophageal reflux – status post Nissen fundoplication.

7. Status post nephrectomy 2009 due to renal cell carcinoma – monitored with yearly CT scans.

a. Creatinine averaging 1.4 to 1.5

8. Sonogram 09/19/2012 revealing myofascial disruptions, multiple

areas, and costochondral inflammation.

   a. Nephrectomy complicated by ileus and surgical site
     dehiscence/hernia – requiring repair of same.

9. Pulmonary nodule seen on chest CT scan 2009 and chest x-ray 2011
   – needs followup (patient is a non-smoker).

10. Status post cholecystectomy 2009 – cholelithiasis.

Comment: This patient is a very intelligent and active individual who is understandably perplexed by his ongoing and perpetual health decline over the past 12 years. I do feel that Lyme borreliosis complex is contributing and he would benefit from treatment targeting the multiple premorphic infections involved with Lyme borreliosis complex.

Prior to reinitiating antimicrobial therapy, I do feel it is imperative to obtain additional information and stabilize his fragile system as much as possible.

The pathophysiology of Lyme Borreliosis Complex was discussed at length today with the patient. The role of stress and inflammation and how it pertains to the disease process, treatment, and recovery were reviewed. Treatment strategies targeting decreasing infection load while strengthening and reorganizing natural immune functioning and facilitating body system repair were discussed. I do feel the patient has benefitted greatly by the aggressive measures implemented by Dr. Lee in this regard.

Lyme borreliosis complex's impact on various body systems including neurologic, GI, musculoskeletal, cardiovascular, endocrine, immunologic were reviewed. The importance of maintaining low systemic inflammation and minimizing "stressors" on the system throughout therapy to improve and strengthen natural immune functioning were reviewed today as well. Treatment goals and expectations were reviewed with the patient and his wife today. I also addressed multiple questions and concerns presented by the patient and his wife.

At this point is it unclear whether the patient will need IV therapy. Certainly, I am concerned given the infections impact on his nervous and gastrointestinal systems. Again at this time I would like to focus over the next 4 – 6 weeks on stabilizing and intensifying his detoxification strategies. The decision of whether or not to implement IV therapy will be determined by his response.

Recommendations: summary

Given lab slip to obtain current information regarding his metabolic, immunologic, nutritional and endocrine status. Thrombophilia screens were included.

Given an order for an MRI scan of the cervical spine with and without contrast to assess for structural abnormalities.

To offer assessment of metabolic activity within his central nervous system, he is given an order for a brain SPECT scan. Unfortunately, facilities are limited in the Midwest and likely the patient will need to arrange this evaluation through an experienced facility such as Reston Hospital in the Washington D.C. area.

Given information to follow a gluten – free lifestyle as we feel this will benefit not only his gastrointestinal system but also further help to decrease his systemic inflammatory quotient.

Given referral for a chest CT scan with contrast to reassess his pulmonary nodules.

Encouraged to use CPAP nightly for entire night. Maintaining adequate sleep architecture is crucial to his immunologic recovery.

Detoxification strategies were discussed including the use of infrared sauna, methylcobalamin, Epsom Salt baths, lymphatic drainage massage, burbur drops, etc.

The patient was given multiple prescriptions for nutritional support and for his neurological health.

The above is just a small part of her very extensive and detailed written report. There was one thing in her report that I disagreed with though. She had written that I had kept excellent records of my medical health and had a good understanding of my condition. That was all Julie. One of the blessings of being married to a nurse who was so determined to restore my health was her meticulous record keeping and her continued quest for answers.

Part of the closing conversation with Kim was concerning my work load during treatment. By now I had heard several times that I could expect to feel worse before I felt better. It was anticipated that the fatigue would increase, that there would be times of nausea and just feeling sick. Very likely I'd have days when I would not get out of bed. Kim suggested that working part-time with very flexible hours would be ideal. She was clear that stressful situations would be counterproductive to the healing process. While my workload was my decision, she was clear that cutting back was important.

Returning home, my first instruction was to do an extensive blood lab. I called a local lab and set an appointment. I arrived a few minutes before my appointment and noticed about five people sitting in the waiting area. I thought that this would be a long wait. The lady doing the labs finished with one patient and then called me. Since I had an appointment I was being moved up in front of the others waiting. It was a bit uncomfortable to walk past the others and into the office to get started. There was only one person on duty that day in the lab. This poor woman was responsible for writing the order, drawing the blood, and labeling the vials of blood.

One look at my order and she said, "You must be kidding. I have never drawn this many vials from anyone. In fact, I am not even allowed to do so as it is more blood than we can draw in one sitting." I pleaded with her as I was desperate to have this lab sent in, so she agreed to call her supervisor who thankfully gave her the okay because of my weight. The next step was to methodically work through the order looking up the many draws that were new to her. This required numerous calls for clarification. Finally, all of the lab order was clarified so we could begin to draw blood.

She took 27 vials from my right arm and then that vein dried up, so she finished the last five from my left arm. Several needed to be refrigerated immediately, as she kept everything in order. After checking the computer she began to run off the labels. The labels extended down to the floor, and she smiled and said, "First time that has happened." When there were just a few more labels to print the printer ran out, and she had to get another ring of labels from the closet. After the labels were printed, she finished putting the labels on each vial and I was ready to go.

My appointment had been at 9:00 am and now it was noon. I apologized for the great hassle I had been, and she was very sweet about it. She was just one more example of a gracious and qualified health provider who was willing to do whatever was asked of her. She never complained, just went about her work very methodically, carefully, and in a good spirit.

When I walked out of the office and across the foyer, which was now crowded with people, I did not make eye contact with anyone. I just looked at the door and hoped to make it out without any problems. They must have been furious with me for having taken up almost the whole morning.

Help

At the next congregational oversight board meeting I shared with them that I would be starting treatment in January and would not be able to work full-time for at least the first part of the treatment. We talked of persons we could contact to help carry the pastoral load if I were to cut to 50%. We agreed that I would call Mel Shetler, a recently retired local pastor who was a good fit for Clinton Frame.

I called Mel, and he agreed to meet with me the next day. I shared with him my situation and that the Oversight Board was hoping he could join our pastoral team during the time when I would be part-time. We were asking him to provide pulpit presence, meet regularly with the pastoral team, be available for some Pastoral care, and be a support to me. He agreed to get back with me after a few days but felt very positive about the conversation and the call from our congregational oversight board. It was good to talk with Mel, but it was a stark reminder to me that this treatment period was coming at a high cost to me emotionally. While I knew it was necessary, I had great difficulty in admitting that I would have to let go of a part of my pastoral ministry for a season.

When he agreed to do it a few days later, I asked if his wife, Edna, was supportive. I understand how important a supportive spouse is in pastoral ministry. He smiled and said that he had told Edna about a week before the phone call that he had a sense from God that Clinton Frame was going to ask him to help in some way. My request was not a surprise, and both he and Edna were at peace knowing that this was God's call on him at this time. What a blessing for me that God had already given Mel that sense of calling. As difficult as it was for me to have to cut back, it helped to know that Mel would be able to serve the congregation. I appreciate what both Mel's and God's presence meant for me personally, as it helped me to relax over months of harsh treatment. I am grateful for Mel's ministry to Clinton Frame for the ten months I received IV therapy.

December 4 of 2012, I had a phone consult with Kim. In her report from that conversation she began with, "Terry has been extremely compliant in implementing recommendations and getting ordered studies done at this time." It was true that I was willing to do anything they asked me to do. I was desperate to get better and believed this could be the answer. Also, Julie was extremely vigilant to make sure I was following the protocol. Kim noted that I continued to be concerned about my abdominal cramps and diarrhea which occurred about three times a week and increased my probiotics to 50 billion units per day and doubled my Saccharomyces dosage.

Cramps and diarrhea had become a way of life for me, for many years. I was always fearful when I got up front at church, especially to preach, fearing one of these episodes would hit during the sermon. Later, during the treatment when Kim asked me about these episodes, I told her that I was doing better. The amount of time I had to get to the restroom had gone from seconds to minutes. She smiled and said, "Well, that is an improvement." At this consult I also expressed concern over increasing fatigue. She believed this had more to do with my sleep patterns than with the neurotrophic regime.

Fatigue worsened, continually, overwhelming any experience. It was rare to get through a day without a nap in the afternoon and evening meetings were becoming more difficult. I knew I was having trouble focusing and at times during meetings would be keenly aware of my desire to just lay my head back and close my eyes. I could be talking with a person one-on-one and my head would hurt and all I wanted to do was end the conversation. At this point, I did not understand how much greater the fatigue would become during treatment.

In Kim's second report she wrote that she continued to be concerned that I might be a candidate for intravenous therapy, given my neurologic involvement, as well as the state of my gastrointestinal system. She discussed IV therapy with us during the consult, and I had a sense that it was moving that direction. She talked at length of the importance of obtaining adequate medical, social, financial and logistical support prior to and during therapy, noting that I am extremely fortunate to have the ongoing support of Dr. Lee and Dr. Anderson, and the strong support of family and friends. I was also given information on how to apply for financial assistance. She again highlighted how imperative it was to stabilize and balance my system as soon as possible.

One of the greatest assets I had going into treatment was the amazing support of family and friends. My children were fully supportive of me. I remember Lindsy regularly telling me how much she appreciated that I was making the effort to take care of my health. All of my children expressed concern for me. My son Eric, who is one of few words, would always simply ask, "How are you doing, Dad?" On hard days ahead, that was all I needed to hear. I knew how much they loved me and how much they wanted their father to be healthy. They want me around for years to come. This gave me the motivation I needed to get through the months ahead.

I also continued to feel complete support from the congregational oversight board, pastoral team, and the congregation. I am fully aware and thankful for the fact that anytime I made a request of the Board they always granted it as they put my well-being first. I know the pastoral team picked up extra work without complaining. People in the congregation were constantly letting me know they were praying for me and offering words of encouragement. Without the support from all of those around me the treatment that was about to begin would have been much more difficult to endure.

Finances are another major stressor in treatment for chronic Lyme disease. Julie and I were fortunate to have the financial means to begin treatment. Since chronic Lyme is not recognized by the CDC and the medical establishment, treatment is not covered by health insurances. All the doctor visits and all of the IV therapy had to be paid out-of-pocket. The cost of the IV therapy and doctor visits was over $70,000. This does not include travel expenses and nights in hotels. I know that many people lose their life savings or sell their homes in order to get treatment. This is one of the great tragedies of the unwillingness of the medical world to accept that this horrible disease is real.

Since we did not turn in any of the IV treatment or doctor visits, I believe our insurance company never realized what I was being treated for. It was a gift that they did pay for all of my many blood draws, lab costs, and oral medication. These totaled well over $100,000. I am fully aware of the many blessings I received that made it possible for me to begin treatment with as little stress as possible.

More than anything else, I had a wife that would stand by me, care for me, and see me through the months of treatment. She never let me go to any appointment alone. Julie was determined to hear what the doctor said and knew what questions to ask. In all the months of organizing my medications, trips to the pharmacy, and the countless hours she dedicated to my care, she never complained but was so positive. Whenever someone asked her if she had retired from nursing I would always say, "She is taking care of me and I am a full-time job." I do not know how people make it through this treatment alone.

Love

Finally, the long-awaited date for my treatment to begin arrived. January 09, 2013. We left after church to go to D.C., about a ten-hour drive, for an early Monday morning appointment in Reston, Virginia for a spect brain scan. For some reason, I always insisted on waiting until after church to leave, even though that meant a very late night arrival in D.C. Looking back, I know this was not fair to Julie who had to do all the driving while I slept.

I think not missing Sunday morning service was my way of not giving into the disease any more than I had to. It would not stop me from being in church on Sunday morning. As pastor, I felt a great responsibility and desire to be with my congregation for worship, to be the shepherd, as that lovely nurse had so long ago called me.

That night, as Julie drove, I woke up and heard a song that Julie was playing over and over again from a favorite CD. *Healing Rain is Coming Down* by Michael W. Smith. *Healing rain is coming down, Healing rain is coming down. I'm not afraid, I'm not afraid.* Julie had tears in her eyes and said the song was her prayer. She believed we were finally starting a treatment that would bring healing. *Healing rain is falling down, faith is rising.* I fell in love with her all over again. This amazingly strong woman who had stuck with me, with persistence and love, was making this journey towards healing with me. We were finally on our way to begin treatment for Lyme disease.

After our initial consult, all I wanted to do was get the therapy started, but I understood the need to build up my debilitated system and for further testing. We first needed to do the spect brain scan in Virginia. Dr. Jemsek had ordered the scan and wanted it done at the Reston Hospital as they knew what he was looking for. A spect scan is a nuclear imaging test that incorporates a radioactive substance and a special camera to create 3-D pictures. It shows the blood flow in any organ and highlights inflammation. We needed a clearer picture of how active the Lyme disease was in my brain.

We found our way through the huge hospital to the correct area for the procedure. The results from the scan were critical as it revealed four areas of inflammation in my brain. Dr. Jemsek said this was the only really accurate test for confirming that one had Lyme disease. This was a relief to me as I was always looking for actual data to say I had this disease.

Based on the scan results, we would begin the treatment with IV therapy and treat it as aggressively as possible. I asked him if there are any risks from the inflammation, and he said that any time there is inflammation in the brain, one is at risk of strokes. I've seen the devastating results of strokes in a number of person's lives, and all I could say was, let's get started.

The next morning we were at George Washington University Hospital in downtown D.C. to have the central line placed. A central line was inserted into my right upper chest just below the clavicle. The line than runs into the vena cava which empties into the right atrium of the heart. It would place the medication at the exact spot where it would be the most effective. The central line extended out of my chest about 5 inches and was where we would connect the IV line each time I received therapy. It really is a great way to get an IV.

The line required care, and I had to cover it with plastic each time I took a shower. The risk of a central line is infection and because of its location an infection can make one very sick quickly. I would later experience just how quickly one's temperature can rise with a central line infection.

The young aide who wheeled me to surgery was an energetic talkative guy, and we immediately connected and engaged in conversation. When we entered the surgery room, I heard fairly loud jazz music and commented that I had never heard music like this before in a surgery room. The aide replied that he used to sing jazz, but now he only sings in the gospel choir in his church. I said, "Good for you," and told him I am a pastor who appreciates those who use their musical gifts and voices in the church. Music is such an important part of worship.

He then told the rest of those in the room, "This guy is a pastor. Let's take special care of him." A woman down towards my feet said, "Praise God, I have been a Christian for three years," and a man's voice from behind said, "I am a Jew but became a follower of Jesus last year, and my life has totally changed." Who would have ever expected a surgery room in inner city D.C. to be a place of praise and exalting the name of Jesus? Healing rain is falling down, faith is rising, I sang to myself.

After the central line was placed Julie and I had lunch and went over to the clinic for the long-awaited moment of beginning treatment. I received my first IV antibiotic after another extensive interview with Dr. Jemsek who told us he would monitor my progress at the beginning. They always gave me the first dose of each new antibiotic to make sure that I did not have an allergic reaction. We waited a half hour after receiving the antibiotic before being checked out.

We had a suitcase full of antibiotic bags, prescriptions for more oral drugs, and all the paraphernalia we needed to give the IVs for the upcoming month. The clinic nurses were very detailed and careful in counting out all the different items in our suitcase. We always had exactly what we needed.

We drove home yet that night. I am sure I had something on Wednesday I thought I needed to be back for. We did this trip as quickly as possible, and the next time we did it in two days. After that we decided we would give ourselves an extra day in D.C. for each appointment. That way, we might be able to relax and recuperate. I was beginning to learn that we had to slow down as we were in this for the long haul.

Over the next couple of years, we would make eighteen trips to Washington D.C., and we preferred driving the ten hours instead of flying. We flew one time and it was a security nightmare. Each IV bag had to be swiped and tested for explosives, and we had to hand carry everything onto the plane.

---

from Julie:

Each time we traveled to the Jemsek Specialty Clinic we took an empty suitcase to fill with IV bags, tubing, dressing changes, etc. We usually left the clinic with a bulging suitcase and a box or bag. The staff was excellent in teaching the administration of IVs and making sure that we had exactly what we needed until we came back the next month. This is just another way that Dr. Jemsek helps his patients. It would have cost tens of thousands of dollars or more had we had to go through an infusion service for the IVs and supplies. The savings to us were huge, as insurance would cover none of it.

Terry's treatment also required a liter bag of lactated ringers for each day he didn't take antibiotics, and we had to get these elsewhere.

The solution was for flushing his system and helping to detox his body. It was a challenge to find a local pharmacy to work with us on this. To my surprise, our local Kroger store pharmacist kindly ordered Lactated Ringers for us by the case.

Almost monthly we had new prescriptions to fill that even our Walgreen pharmacists had never heard of, so needless to say we developed a good relationship. One pharmacist was always interested in Terry's treatment and protocol. Each time I came in with something new to him we had a laugh. Treating someone for Lyme in Goshen, Indiana was an oddity.

Pulsing

Returning home, we tried to get into our new treatment routine called "pulsing" which means there are on and off times of receiving antibiotics. The protocol was very complicated, and I am so thankful that Julie could understand it and keep it organized. I wonder how Lyme patients who are alone are able to do the treatment. Each day had a different combination of pills and IVs. For me it would have been impossible to manage, especially when feeling so sick. There were times in the treatment when I would take up to 30 pills twice a day. On top of this was the IV therapy. The first morning after we would return home, Julie would spend hours going over the treatment plan and writing it out on her computer in a way we could understand more easily.

We started reading books about Lyme to educate ourselves, and sometimes this helped us manage information and feel less overwhelmed. Books written by people who have experienced Lyme disease were especially helpful. We found there to be a lot of controversy in different treatments, but trusted and believed that we chose the treatment best for me. We were also informed by Dr. Jemsek that Lyme disease is sexually transmitted, and that Julie's health also needed to be monitored closely. As we became more knowledgeable, especially Julie, we couldn't help but wonder whether the severe hormonal imbalances Julie experienced for more than ten years, and even today, are likely due to Lyme. It is tempting at times to question whether her normal aches and pains may be Lyme-related.

The first round of treatment I took one IV antibiotic twice a day on Monday, Wednesday, and Friday during the first week. The second round of treatment another IV was added on those same days. This is what made the treatment confusing. The second week I was taking three antibiotic IVs on my treatment days, each taking at least 30 minutes to administer. On the off days, I was to receive a liter of lactated ringer to flush my system which took at least 90 minutes to administer. This meant that I was hooked up to an IV bag every day.

Part of the reality of IV therapy is just the amount of time it takes. Later in treatment I would have five antibiotic bags in one day. Some in the morning and then again in the evening, with flushing between all of the bags and at the end. I also began to go to Crossroad Healing Arts twice a week to receive an IV detox that took at least an hour and a half. The formula for the detox was written by Dr. Jemsek, and Crossroad Healing Arts was gracious to get and administer the IV.

With a treatment such as this, one needs solid teamwork between the specialist physician and your local doctor. Along with the IV there were various oral antibiotics. The first round I was introduced to the drug that all of Dr. Jemsek's patients become very familiar with, Flagyl, which I took only on Thursday and Friday of week one. Flagyl is a drug used to fight many different bacteria and parasites. It can have strong side effects of dizziness, upset stomach, and nausea. Fortunately, I did not react strongly to this drug as it was part of my protocol the entire treatment time. For me, it was just another one of the drugs I was now taking often, but had never heard of before.

The routine was, on treatment for two weeks, and then two weeks of recovery. The second week of recovery I would return to D.C. for a check-up and to receive instructions and medicine for the next round. During the first round, I did not take the lactated ringer on my off weeks. Julie and I argued over this one. She was sure I was supposed to keep taking it, and I was just as sure that I was to only take it during my weeks of treatment. At the next appointment, Dr. Jemsek asked me why I didn't take the ringer the last two weeks. I said because I was on holidays. They referred to the recovery weeks as "holidays." He smiled and said, "Reverend, that doesn't mean you don't need to flush your system. Every day you do not get IV antibiotics you need to get a lactated ringer." I realized, as I actually already knew, that Julie was always right when it came to my treatment protocol. It also hit me that this treatment was going to be very time consuming, requiring at least one IV every single day.

We returned to D.C. for another consultation on Feb. 7th. The weather forecast was for a major snowstorm on the east coast with D.C. to get between 24 and 30 inches of snow. We talked about not going as it seemed the city would be shut down but decided to take our chances.

As was our custom, we left after church, arriving Sunday night, and stayed in a hotel about 30 minutes outside the city. It was snowing when we arrived, and the forecast had not changed. At that point, it seemed our trip was in vain, as the city was closing down for the expected storm.

In the morning, we woke up to good news. During the night it had warmed up to the upper 30s so the snow had turned to rain. The pouring rain slowed traffic, and it was a mess getting downtown to the clinic, but at least it was open. It rained hard all day. Had the temperatures not risen there would have been a lot of snow. Our good fortune with the weather was continuing. *Healing rain is falling down, faith is rising.*

In his report of this consultation Dr. Jemsek wrote that it was important to get my extensive medical history in order, as mine is one of the more complex ones he had seen. Dr. Jemsek wrote, "This gentleman has certainly had his share of medical issues, and one can't help but think that much of this is due to the underlying borreliosis." My multiple hypothalamic and pituitary issues were noted and I was ordered to increase my cortisol prescription. During the consultation he told me that the treatment will tax healthy adrenals and since mine are already shot, I would need extra help to get me through it.

Part of what made my case more complex and why I required close monitoring was that I now had only one kidney. My creatinine level (creatinine baseline level reveals kidney function) was already slightly elevated, so they watched this closely as we had to protect the one kidney I still had. Dr. Jemsek also noted what he referred to as "significant cardiac issues" and the "abnormal brain spect scan which was consistent with diffuse encephalopathy associated with neuroborreliosis." At this consult I was informed that the IV therapy was anticipated to last six to eight months.

---

from Julie:

I was judicious each month on return from Washington D.C. Even before unpacking sometimes, I would run off calendars and write out the treatment protocols in great detail so that we could remember. There were supplements that Terry had to take for the first eight days, and two medications he only took on Thursday and Friday of week one. Each week's schedule was complex and different. The calendars I made were color coded by IVs, oral medications, liquid medications and even lab tests which Terry had to do with each round of treatment. Then there was the ordering of many different neutraceuticals and herbal products that came from various companies. Thank goodness for the ability to order these via Internet. We were thankful for my background in nursing and the organizational skills that I learned over years of nursing. Terry always made sure that I knew how grateful he is for this and has thanked me more often than I know.

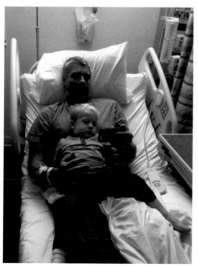

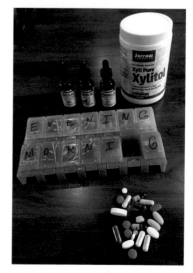

A rainbow over Georgetown in Washington D.C. This was a promise of God's presence. A promise of hope given to Julie & I after a disappointing day.

My World

Fatigue began to settle in during the first two weeks of treatment. If I had no morning appointments, I would sleep until 10:00, often sleeping ten hours a night. One of the blessings for me was that I was able to sleep, and sleep well during treatment. I know that for some Lyme patients the opposite is true. I also had low grade fevers, and my body thermostat was off, which caused flushing and feeling hot, especially at night. Julie is not so sure, but I believe I can fully relate to how women feel who have "hot flashes." I experienced increased numbness in my feet, and it was increasingly easy for me to accept that I would have to be part-time at work during this part of the treatment.

The consultation with Dr. Jemsek went well. He asked if I had been to the emergency room since he had last seen me, and I was glad to be able to say no. He was pleased with how I had handled the first round, except that my creatinine level had increased due to the one antibiotic, so he removed it from my protocol and said we would use alternatives. I appreciated his vigilance on behalf of my kidney. He ordered a new IV antibiotic which I received in his clinic before leaving, and added two oral antimalarial medications, Mepron and Artemisinin, that I would learn had a drastic effect on how I felt.

In filling the prescriptions, Julie got to know our pharmacist very well. It was typical for him to say that he had never heard of this medication, and if he was familiar with it, he would say there is no way they want me to take this large of a dosage. He then would call the clinic to verify the prescription and find that the prescription was indeed written correctly. I very much appreciated the effort and care of the pharmacist who worked hard and filled every prescription.

Mepron was the medication most difficult to take. It was a gooey fluorescent yellow semi-liquid, that for me, did not go down easy. I was to follow it immediately with a fatty food like peanut butter. After taking the Mepron even peanut butter tasted bad. It would make me nauseated and just feel awful. The inside of my mouth would break out in sores, affecting my taste buds so much that I would not be able to taste food for at least a week after finishing a round. I'd wonder what the inside of my stomach looked like. And Mepron was terribly expensive; one small bottle cost $1300. I am not sure how many bottles I took, but it was a good number. Its main purpose was to treat the co-infection, babesia, which seemed to be a critical issue for me.

Babesia directly affects the liver which is why at each appointment they carefully checked my liver. I am sure it was worth taking Mepron in the long run, but of all the medications I had it was by far the worst. After treatment when I met with a new nephrologist she read my chart and said, "So you have taken Mepron." She went on to say, "That is some awful stuff." I asked her if she had ever taken it. She told me that when she went home to Ghana for a vacation she was to take Mepron as a way to avoid getting Malaria. She took it two weeks and quit. There was no way she could keep taking it because it did so many strange things to her body and mind. It was kind of nice to be able to talk with someone who knew what Mepron is like.

When taking so many drugs it is hard to know how each specific one is affecting you. I do believe the Mepron caused me to feel like my head was spinning, and my thought processes were off. The weeks of Mepron were the weeks I should not have been leading worship or preaching as my words could come out wrong. It also made me nauseated with overall flu-like symptoms. It is hard to describe, but I would just feel terrible.

During this round of treatment, I had low-grade fever a lot of the time with the highest being 101.5. I also had boat rocking syndrome, which means my equilibrium was off and I felt like I was walking on a boat. As with all symptoms, there were times when they were worse and times when they were better. I never knew what each day would bring. My hands and feet became even colder than normal. I started wearing heavy socks to bed which is something I deplore. My fatigue continued to increase, and I was having involuntary jerking at night. The medical term for the involuntary jerking is herxing. Herxing is the body's way of ridding itself of toxins.

I had to maintain a positive attitude and accept that these were all signs that the medication was beginning to work at the bacteria in my body and brain. This was something I had to focus on throughout treatment. Feeling worse for a time, meant that I would return to a normal life in the future. Because of the hope of a better tomorrow, I was determined to go through whatever the treatment might bring.

We returned to D.C. the first of March for another consultation and to start another round of treatment. Dr. Jemsek was pleased with how well I was managing the treatment and how well my body was enduring it. He assured me that the symptoms I was experiencing were normal and a good sign that the medications were having intended effects. I complained to him that my body could not yet tolerate physical labor. He explained that I was too far down the oxidative stress curve to get the kind of treatment benefit I would need to tolerate physical labor. For me, the inability to go outside and work was a major loss. He assured me that this would change in two to three months. He once again noted their careful watch of my creatinine as it was still elevated but not to a dangerous level.

He gave me a new protocol for the next round of treatment. The major change was that I would be two weeks on two weeks off and then two weeks on again. This meant I would not be returning to D.C. until the middle of April. He added a new drug to intensify my babesia program. It was becoming obvious that this co-infection was a major part of my treatment plan.

We began the third round of treatment and then a crisis struck.

During the night, after my second IV of round three, I woke up with a high fever. I had never experienced anything like this. I lay in bed shaking and my teeth chattering, and I was thinking, well he said this round might be worse and I guess he was right. After a while the fever broke and the uncontrollable shaking stopped. I fell back asleep.

The next afternoon I hooked up to my IV to receive the lactated ringer. I was holding our three-month-old grandson and thought we would both have a good nap as I received the IV. Within a few minutes, I woke up with uncontrollable shaking again. I called for Julie and my sister Marlene to come and get Michael as I could not hold him with the convulsions that were starting. We checked my fever. It was over 104, and the convulsions were coming faster and stronger. When we checked again it was 105, and a few minutes later 105.5. Julie was on the phone calling the clinic to see what we should do, and I asked Marlene to go get some cold water to put on my head. She came, in her caring manner, with a washcloth and water and placed the damp washcloth carefully on my head.

At this point I wondered if I was going to survive. I wondered how high a fever can go and a body endure it. I told her to forget the wash cloth and pour the glass of water on my head. She didn't want to do it. She's just too nice to want to do such a thing, so I yelled, "Just pour it on me!" With a pained looked on her face she poured a good amount on my head, and when it ran down my back it was a shock to my body and I stood right up out of that recliner. Julie came in and said we had to get to the hospital as fast as possible. I knew she was right and wanted to go. However, as we went out the door and into the garage I said, "No matter what they say I am going to be in church tomorrow morning." I had worked hard at helping to plan a special service in which the whole congregation would experience a "Passover meal," and I so badly wanted to be a part of the service.

In the emergency room, they quickly got my fever under control, and after being there for several hours they released me to go home. So my wish was granted, and I was able to go to the service in the morning. I really did not feel good Sunday morning, but I enjoyed the service. One of the songs we sang was "Blessed Be Your Name." This song has meant a lot to me over the years as it calls us to be able to bless God through the valley and mountain top experiences of life.

When we went home, Marlene told me that she was so glad to be at the service and how the music spoke to her in a different way in light of our experience the afternoon and evening before. She wondered how I felt singing some of the songs in the midst of my journey. Actually, the worship songs gave me great comfort and hope. That is why I insisted on being in worship, even when my body and mind were not well.

Blessed be your name in the land that is plentiful when the streams of abundance flow. Blessed be your name. Blessed be your name when I'm found in the desert place, when I walk through the wilderness. Blessed be your name. Every blessing you pour out I'll turn back to praise, when the darkness closes in Lord, still I will say, Blessed be the name of the Lord, Blessed be your glorious name. Blessed be your name when the sun's shining down on me, when the world's all that it should be, Blessed be your name. Blessed be your name on the road marked with suffering, though there's pain in the offering Blessed be your name. Every blessing you pour out I will turn to praise. When the darkness closes in, Lord, still I will say Blessed be your name.

This song speaks so powerfully of remembering God's blessings in all of life. Sometimes blessings are equated with things that make us happy, but to be blessed is so much more than that. I continue to live a blessed life as I struggle through all that Lyme can do to my body and well-being. One of the amazing blessings throughout my treatment was to be able to worship with my congregation every Sunday morning. When I began the treatment I assumed there would be Sundays when I would not be able to make it to church. Thankfully, that did not happen.

That Sunday afternoon the hospital called and said my blood results were back. I had a dangerous infection in my central line and needed to return to the hospital immediately. I said we were having guests for dinner and I would come as soon as we were done eating. The hospital staff said, "No, you are to come immediately," so Julie and I went to the hospital and my family who were coming over for dinner ate without us. That night about 2:30 I awoke and got up to sit in a rocker since I was unable to sleep. I was discouraged wondering why these things happen to me and again just longing to be healthy. I opened my Bible to the Psalms and it fell open to Psalm 73:29: *My health may fail and my spirit grow weak, but God is the strength of my heart. You are mine forever.* That verse brought overwhelming peace to me that night, the last line grabbing my attention. God belongs to me. God is mine.

We often say that we belong to God, but the reverse is also true. *You are mine forever.* This was all I needed that night, and it was a verse I would say over and over again many times in the weeks and months ahead. After a prayer, I went back to bed. The next morning Marlene came to see me to talk. When she sat down my opening words were "Welcome to my world." She looked at me, compassion in her eyes, and said, "Yes, this is your world, isn't it."

"We Will"

It was during this hospital stay that I came face to face with the resistant medical establishment. The infectious disease doctor who was overseeing my care came in and noticed the large binder containing my medical history. He asked if he could read it, and for the next almost thirty minutes carefully read through it all including my current treatment. He then looked at me and said, "I am going to be as polite as possible, but I have an obligation to let you know that you do not have Lyme disease. In fact, chronic Lyme disease does not exist." This was followed by a 20-minute lecture about how ridiculous the treatment was and essentially told me that the doctor who was putting me through this was a quack.

I finally held my hand up and told him he needed to stop. I continued, saying that I have complete trust and faith in my doctor who was treating me for chronic Lyme disease. I told him I was convinced I needed this treatment, that I believed it was my only hope at getting better, and that since I believed in it I was going to complete the treatment regardless of what he might say. He looked at me with a condescending smile and said, "If you want to be this doctor's guinea pig, feel free, but I wouldn't recommend it." And with that, he left.

I was overwhelmed by his ignorance and superior attitude. I had heard and read that this was the medical establishment's belief, but this was the first time I had met it in the flesh. It made me angry but also grateful for the doctors who were overseeing my care. I am so thankful for the doctors I met who cared enough about people that they are willing to take the risks to provide loving, caring treatment even when the medical establishment stands against them and calls them quacks. Doctors like Dr. Jemsek are willing to treat people who other doctors refuse to treat, sometimes at great personal sacrifice.

The next morning when the infectious disease doctor came into my room, Julie was there, and she was mad. It was his turn to listen, and I give him credit in that he listened for many minutes as she let him know what she believed. When she was done he simply said, "You are wrong, but if you want to continue the treatment you can." We both responded, "We will."

Later, after I was able to process better, I wrote him a letter. I began by thanking him for his care in treating my central line infection. He had diagnosed and treated the infection, and for that I was grateful. But, I also wanted to address how I felt about his lecture concerning my treatment for Lyme. I started with the same words he had used: "I am going to be as polite as possible, but on behalf of the tens of thousands who suffer from chronic Lyme disease, I have an obligation to share with you the truth of the horrible effects of chronic Lyme and how difficult it is to find treatment because of a medical establishment that refuses to recognize that it exists." I doubt if my letter had any effect on what he believes. It just felt good to voice some of my frustration and my deep desire that all doctors take chronic Lyme disease seriously.

I was in the hospital only three days, but the disappointment was that my central line had to be removed. A doctor came in and removed it and then the treatment was interrupted for about three weeks until I could have a new one inserted. Putting the treatment off three weeks was a big disappointment. I so much wanted to get the treatment phase behind me.

During this time, the brachial plexitis reoccurred in my right shoulder. Once again, I had intense pain for about a week and then numbness and weakness to my right arm. Even though this was only April, I knew that I would not have strength in the fall to pull back my bow. As a result, archery season was off for a second season. Now that was true suffering.

During the next round, nausea increased, but at least the medication I took for nausea seemed to help. My cognitive issues also intensified with more brain fog. Brain fog is hard to describe. One afternoon when I went to the refrigerator I found the mail on the top shelf. I asked Julie why she put the mail in the refrigerator and was told, in no uncertain terms, that she wasn't the one who put it there.

When trying to do a pastoral visit one morning, I was unable to find the condo of the lady I was needing to visit. I had been to her home twice before but could not locate it. Frustrated, I finally gave up and went back to the church. During moments of brain fog, Julie would have to repeat things many times. My short-term memory was limited, to say the least.

There were several times I had to focus and speak slower than normal during public speaking. This was especially important during weddings and funerals as those are events when you cannot make a mistake. I remember Casey telling me that I had been a bit off while officiating one of my nephew's weddings. He commented that usually I am so clear and right on, but I'd had some lapses that day.

One time when having a discussion with two of the pastors on my team, one mentioned that I had forgotten something. The other playfully commented, "That is just Terry." I understood, but sometimes comments like that hurt a bit. The mental and emotional effects of the disease were the most difficult to manage.

The fatigue continued to intensify, but I was assured that this was a result of my system's ongoing battle with the Lyme borreliosis and heightened systemic inflammation. Kim and Dr. Jemsek were clear that they believed I was making clinical progress and stressed the importance of minimizing sources of stress as we moved forward with treatment.

---

from Julie:

There were many times when Terry's brain fog was so evident in the morning before going to work that I wondered how he would manage. This would happen even years before he was diagnosed with Lyme, but became particularly bad during treatment. Sometimes on a Sunday morning I would pray as he headed out the door, "Okay God, this one is all yours." It certainly was with the help of God, as he was struggling so much physically.

Terry became quite good, actually very good, at appearing normal during the Sunday morning hours when he was really feeling sick. But then he crashed into his recliner when he got home and slept all afternoon. As time went on, I became more and more restrictive of any other activities outside of his work demands. It was hard, but often I turned down invitations to meals or other events simply because I knew Terry could not tolerate more than work.

I also realized that our social life was dwindling. We did less and less with our friends, partly because of many evening meetings a pastor has. But, it was also to guard any free time for needed rest.

Stress and Support

S tress was something that I continually tried to work through. I could reduce hours, but reducing stress was more difficult. The role of lead pastor demands carrying a variety of the congregation's areas of stress, and this did not change during my treatment. At the same time, the congregation continued to be very supportive and caring.

I cannot begin to describe the many ways I was cared for, and the words of encouragement and supportive prayer I received every day. The Jr. High Youth Group came and raked our yard, a major task as we have a large yard with many trees. Each spring there are many baskets of sticks and hickory nuts to rake up before mowing can begin. Twice Sunday School classes from the church came and raked vast amounts of leaves in the fall. It was humbling, but greatly appreciated. As difficult as treatment was, I know it was more bearable because of the congregation's continual support.

In June, I developed another central line infection. When I was getting ready for church one Sunday morning I knew I was not doing well, and my fever was slightly elevated. I taught a membership class that morning during the Sunday School hour, and I knew my fever was going up. I was chilling and sweating at the same time, but the class was important and I wanted to get through it.

After the service, I stayed for a fellowship meal with Sunday School Class leaders. I had a presentation which I cut short due to just feeling lousy. After the meeting adjourned, I hurried home, and Julie immediately took my temperature. It was 102.5 which meant we headed to the hospital. They were able to get my fever to drop in the emergency room, but because of my previous hospitalization for infection they kept me overnight until the blood culture came back. Tests confirmed that I had another infection, so once again the central line was removed and I was placed on different antibiotics. Removing the central line was especially discouraging as it meant another interruption in treatment.

Three weeks later the central line was reinserted by Dr. Diener. I asked him why he believed I was having trouble with contaminating the line. Julie and I were following protocol and being careful when hooking the line to the IV bags. His reply was that living on the farm, working outside, and being around animals was a different lifestyle than most people who were living with central lines. He felt that with my lifestyle the line could easily become contaminated. Again, another honest and cherished conversation with my cousin doctor.

Julie began an internet search to find a solution and discovered caps that could be placed on the receiver end of the line between treatments. The caps had a disinfectant pad to keep the line sterile. It was a great discovery, and by using the caps I had no more line infections through the rest of treatment. I highly recommend these caps to anyone with a central line.

I continued with the monthly visits to D.C. through November 2013. From June through September my symptoms were at their worse. My equilibrium was often off, and it felt like I was back to walking on a boat. Sunday mornings when I led worship, I would take a second to steady myself before walking up the steps to the platform. I remember several times when I held on to the pulpit to regain balance. My pressure headaches and brain fog increased, and public speaking became more difficult. I had to focus intensely to have my words come out in a way that made sense. Although, I misspeak from time to time when speaking publicly under normal circumstances, during this time I was especially inclined to do so.

One Sunday morning I was trying to give an announcement about some of our youth selling tickets for Port-a-Pit chicken. Instead of Port-a-Pit I said, "Port-a-Pot chicken." The congregation began to chuckle, and I knew I had said something wrong but didn't have a clue what it was. I looked at Julie and she mouthed the words "Port-a-Pit," and I realized my mistake. I corrected the words, and then the congregation felt they had permission to laugh out loud. As always, people were very gracious and understanding. I tried to be kind and patient with myself.

Rest helped. The only relief for the intense pressure headaches frequent during this period was to sit in my recliner with my eyes closed. I would often take afternoon breaks to do this. I was always in this position when receiving IV bags, and this built-in twice-a-day rest was one of the blessings of IV treatment.

During this time I was also doing weekly lymph massages. The lymph system is a complicated and extensive system of fluid just below the skin. Lymph massage helps keep the fluid flowing and was an important part of my detox regimen. I remember one day entering the home of the massage therapist, turning to go through the door to the massage room, and instead simply walking into the wall. My equilibrium was totally messed up.

I made it into the room, prepared for the massage, and got on the table. When she came in to do the massage she commented that whenever she hears a patient saying, "Help me, Jesus" over and over, she knows he is not doing well. It occurred to me that I had not even been aware that I was saying anything, but I also knew that had become a common phrase for me to think and to pray. After the massage, she wanted to call someone to drive me home, but I insisted that I was okay. Somehow, I drove home and immediately fell asleep for a long nap.

In one of her reports Kim wrote that my hepatosplenomegaly was persistent and needed more follow up. This essentially meant that my liver and spleen continued to be enlarged which was mostly a result of the babesia, and it meant I would continue taking Mepron and other anti-malarials. These were the drugs that I longed to be done with. At this point in the treatment I had no idea how long these drugs would be a part of my protocol. I had hoped that I would get used to the Mepron, but it seemed the longer I took it, the harder it was to get down. The treatment phase was getting very long, and what was even more difficult was I didn't know how much longer it would be.

In July they increased the medication to fight against the biofilm as the bacteria is encased in a biofilm that makes it difficult for the antibiotics to attack effectively. This is just part of the insidious nature of this bacteria and disease. Not only does it mutate to withstand the antibiotic, it has a biofilm as its first layer of protection.

On the Right Track

During my August visit, Kim wrote that I was in pleasant spirits and was eager to discuss the next steps of treatment. She added that I remained highly dedicated and motivated to further my health. This was one of the blessings for me during these months of IV therapy. I was convinced we were on the right track and that the medication was working. Sure, I was a bit frustrated that it was taking so long, but at the same time thankful that the symptoms were not worse.

Some Lyme patients suffered so much more. I give much of the credit to people in my congregation who were committed to praying for me throughout the treatment.

At this point I had a week of severe foot pain and increased pressure behind my right eye, on top of increased herxing—involuntary jerking. I would jerk in my legs at night and in my arms and shoulders during the day. They were not painful, but definitely annoying. Herxing is just one more weird result of Lyme. I learned many new words like "herxing" that I wish I never knew.

The good news was that I was recovering more quickly after weeks of treatment and noticing improvement in how I felt. Mepron continued to increase my fatigue over the weeks of treatment, but with so many medications it's incredibly difficult to tell what combination of meds or circumstances has particular effects. My basal temperature normalized and was down to 98.5. This was a huge blessing as the low-grade fever had been wearing me out.

At my September visit, Dr. Jemsek noted that I was excited and very encouraged by all that was happening with therapy. The month had actually been more difficult than I had expected, but on the other hand, I had a feeling that meant the bacteria was being attacked effectively. I had a deep sense that I was in a battle to regain my health, and that I was slowly winning.

During that month I had lancinating pain in my outer foot and the balls of my feet. It felt like I was walking on marbles again. Plus, my creatinine level was up again, so I was taken off one of the antibiotics. I had gotten to where I could tell when my kidney was struggling because when one's kidney is not doing well it affects your whole being. I was having more hot flashes and sleeping more than the previous months.

But there were also times of hope during this month. During the weeks off treatment, I was rebounding better, and the best thing was that the pain in my back and shoulders was totally gone. Even the large lump on my left shoulder had disappeared. This is when I realized how much pain I had been in for years. The stiffness in my neck was also greatly improved. For years, I had not been able to turn my head which was especially bothersome on the farm when needing to back tractors and trailers.

At the next visit, Dr. Jemsek noted that Julie asked a number of appropriate questions. Actually, that was always true. Julie asked specific questions about medications and symptoms. She would also ask how stress would affect my ability to heal and was always concerned that my continued working was having a negative effect on my healing. Again, I was amazed at Julie's dedication and care, and her dogged determination to get me through this treatment. She was and is my greatest source of strength in so many ways.

October 30, 2013 was a huge and glorious day in my treatment protocol. Again, I met with Dr. Jemsek, who was very positive when we discussed how the month had gone. I was doing much better in all regards. I had some flushing and some jerking, but it was much more controlled than the month before. The pain in my feet was gone. In fact, during this month, Julie and I had just gone to bed and were relaxing when I told her, "I think my foot feels normal, at least how I imagined normal feeling." The numbness came and went for several months, but it was definitely better. I had lived with numb feet for over seven years, so this was a major victory. Fatigue, mental clarity, and pressure headaches had all improved. I got to hear Dr. Jemsek say we are ready to move to the oral phase. After ten months, the IV bags were history. I also got a break from Mepron.

I was anxious to have the central line removed and mentioned that to the nurse who suggested I leave it in for a while just to make sure I was done with the IV therapy. However, when I asked Dr. Jemsek he said, "Remove it as soon as possible." When leaving the clinic I called my favorite surgeon, Dr. Diener, and told him I would be home tomorrow and would like to have the central line removed. He met me in his clinic after hours and removed it. I was so glad to have it gone. It made taking showers so much easier, and I no longer had to worry about infections.

The day I was told I could remove the central line I informed the congregational oversight board. At a church meeting that night the chair announced that my IV therapy was complete. Many people told me of the applause in response to that announcement. Just another example of a supportive congregation.

That Thanksgiving Julie's extended family was together for our annual Thanksgiving celebration. My special sister-in-law, Cindy, had asked

Julie's mother, her siblings, their spouses, and all of our nephews and nieces to write me special notes of support and encouragement. What a blessing to receive all of those kind words from the Bontrager family. Cindy put the notes in pockets with the word "CONGRATULATIONS" written across the front. I am thankful for the wonderful family I married into and for their love. I wish I could remember and include the many words and acts of kindness I received from both sides of our families through my treatment.

With the oral protocol, I was able to return to work full-time. This was primarily due to my feeling so much better without the down times I experienced during the weeks on IV treatment. It was also possible to return to full-time status because I no longer had to be hooked to an IV bag for hours each day. I continued with an aggressive detox regimen. Of course, I had good days and bad days, but more good than bad.

There were times when I would crash. These tended to happen during weeks of stress when pastoral demands of preaching, funerals, and congregational issues were especially intense. I would think I was doing well and then I would find myself in my recliner with my eyes closed. The only way to deal with the crashes was to nap and sleep. My sleep patterns had returned to a more normal eight-hours-a-night instead of the ten I'd found necessary during IV therapy. Managing stress and workload was a major issue as I returned to full-time.

In February of 2014, I had a very positive appointment with Dr. Jemsek and felt I was well on my way to recovery. The protocol of antibiotics was going to be very doable and the anti-malarials were not part of the treatment plan. I was so relieved to be finished with Mepron. Life was indeed much better, and I was feeling in better health than I had for years.

Through the Storm

In June of 2014, I finally came to the end of what I thought would be my oral treatment. When treatment started it was to be six to eight months of IV therapy which ended up being ten, partly due to the two interruptions in treatment caused by central line infections. I now had eight months of oral treatment in addition to that, and when I took my last antibiotics on Friday, June 20th I was ready for a celebration.

Unfortunately, I was in a small Kansas town for a church conference, so my celebration consisted of potato chips and ice tea, alone in my hotel room. I have never been very good at celebrations anyway. At the same time, I was fully aware that the treatment was not really done until Dr. Jemsek said it was done, and I also was living with the reality that over the last two months I had felt my health regressing a bit. I knew the upcoming appointment in D.C. was critical.

I was not surprised at how the appointment with Dr. Jemsek went in early July. In his report he stated that unfortunately, without any clear event, I had begun to deteriorate over the past couple of months. I had become more reactive during treatment with more fatigue. I was also experiencing lots of flushing, hot flashes, pressure headaches, and inability to think clearly. A new nodule had been discovered on the right lobe of my thyroid which when tested was benign.

He diagnosed me as having a relapse of babesia. He anticipated that I would need another three to four rounds of treatment, but encouraged Julie and me that there was no reason why I could not anticipate getting entirely better. So I was back on antibiotics. The other bad news was that I was also back on Mepron, artemisinin, and another anti-malarial five days a week. I knew how these would make me feel and dreaded going through the next four rounds of treatment.

We left the clinic late afternoon and went back to the hotel. I was feeling more depressed than at any point in my treatment. By this appointment, I had thought I would be done. I had never been promised this, but in my own mind I had set that as a hope—if not plan. Instead, I had at least four more months to go, and worst of all was that Mepron was back on my protocol.

We left the hotel and walked to Georgetown to get something to eat. The rain hit and it started to pour just before we got to the restaurant and continued while we ate. Julie was trying to be encouraging but realized that mostly I just needed some time to think. She has a great sense of what I need, and at that point I needed space.

After we were done eating we waited a bit for the rain to stop before heading out to return to the hotel. When we stepped out of the restaurant we saw a beautiful rainbow above the tall buildings of the city. I received it as a sign of hope, one of those signs from God that I was becoming used to, and Julie had the same thought. Yes, we were terribly disappointed, but God was not done with me yet, and I knew I just needed to be faithful and place my trust in him. God's promises are always true and faithful. What I didn't know at that time was that it would be more than a year until my treatment would be over.

The babesia focused therapy was aggressive, and I immediately began to feel the effects. Julie came up with a great idea to help me take the Mepron. She bought empty capsules and filled them with the fluorescent yellow goo. We would sit together at the island in our kitchen, and she would use a syringe to fill the capsules with the awful stuff. I then had to swallow them as quickly as she filled them, because the Mepron immediately began to dissolve the capsules. That is some powerful stuff! This method meant I had to take fifteen more capsules each morning and each evening, but it saved the inside of my mouth from breaking out in sores.

With the aggressive treatment I had intense nausea, my balance seemed off, and headaches, cognitive dysfunction, and intense fatigue were back. This was worse on my weeks of treatment, and it would take me a full week to recover after each treatment cycle.

Once again I was having to steady myself before walking up the steps of the platform in the church sanctuary. Again I was focusing carefully when speaking, and at times I used the pulpit for support. One time when I was saying a prayer and holding tight to the pulpit, I lost my balance and took a step to the side to recover. Our Pastor of Worship, Anita Yoder, saw it and in our weekly review of the worship service said she thought she was going to have to catch me. I guess she was praying with one eye open.

I was surprised at how the treatment was affecting me, and was reminded that once again I was in the midst of an intense battle for my health. It was a battle I was determined to win.

During this time, our congregation continued through a very difficult discernment process that was emotionally draining for me. Our congregation was processing its relationship with the denomination and the discernment required extra work from me in terms of communicating with the pastoral team, lay leaders, and the congregation. I believe that the added stress of this time continued to slow down the overall progress of healing. More than the hours, the emotional toll was affecting me the most. It was the most painful discernment process I have been through in the life of my pastoral ministry at many levels. It got to the very root of my pastoral identity.

At this point in my treatment and pastoral ministry, I often wondered if it might have been better to resign from pastoring before I started treatment for Lyme. Julie often suggested I resign to focus on healing, but she always allowed and supported my decision to continue. I had a deep sense that I needed to stay with the congregation through this stretching time of discernment, but there were many times when I questioned if I was being fair to the congregation to be in the midst of such a harsh treatment while serving as lead pastor. While I felt the congregation needed my leadership, it was also true that I needed the congregation. The love and prayers of the people continued strong, and I believe even strengthened as the treatment time grew longer. They did not grow weary of me and never gave up on me.

One song that became my heart song during this time, both for what I was experiencing as lead pastor and as a Lyme patient, was "Cornerstone." *My Hope is built on nothing less, than Jesus' blood and righteousness. I dare not trust the sweetest frame but wholly lean on Jesus' name. Christ alone, Cornerstone, weak made strong in the Savior's love. Through the storm He is Lord, Lord of all. When darkness seems to hide His face, I rest in His unchanging grace. Through every high and stormy gale, my anchor holds within the veil. Christ alone, Cornerstone, weak made strong in the Savior's love. Through the storm He is Lord, Lord of all.*

This song would lift my spirit, especially in Sunday morning worship with a few great drum rolls. This was my hope. Through the storm, Jesus was my anchor. What I did not realize at the time was that I was headed for yet another health crisis.

from Julie:

When Terry first received the Lyme diagnosis, I pleaded with him to resign as pastor. Generally, he is good at listening to me, but not this time. The church was just in the early stages of discerning some difficult changes, which eventually led to leaving the larger denomination. He was dealing with criticism both from within and outside the church. Any pastor or leader within a church may understand the unbelievable amount of stress that was added during this time.

It was during this time that I had to totally accept Terry's life calling and understood that this was at the core of who he is. His commitment to lead the church he loved through this time was truly sacrificial. Many of the books and information we have read speak to the need to decrease stress and encourage job changes if necessary in order to achieve true healing from this awful disease. But, I also feared he would lose his sense of worth and purpose if he left his position as pastor. So I had to let him go and trust that God would get him through it. We both believe in miracles and that he was able to continue working was itself a miracle. I resolved that God must heal him in spite of the stress.

God With Us

In October Julie and I went on a trip to Italy. It was a trip with her family's company and something I needed to do for Julie. She had given so much to me, and I wanted to experience this time in Italy with her. However, during the trip I did not feel good and felt sluggish and off balance.

A few days after returning home, I had a high fever, loose stools, and burning during urination. I went to the emergency room and was diagnosed with pneumonia due to what they saw in my lungs from a chest x-ray and my high white cell count. I questioned the diagnosis as it seemed to me that I did not have the symptoms of pneumonia and wondered about a urinary infection. I had a phone consult with Kim on November 12th, and she encouraged me to follow-up with my urologist, currently tracking down the culture on my urine taken during the ER visit. She expressed her concern and reminded me how serious a kidney infection would be. She suggested I would probably require hospitalization with IV antibiotic therapy.

I continued to feel worse and the burning during urination became more painful. When the urine culture was complete, they called and told me to return to the hospital. I was admitted for IV therapy for treatment of a kidney infection. I knew this was especially serious in light that I had only one kidney.

The first evening in the hospital my daughter brought me some of my favorite food, but best of all, she brought my two-year-old grandson Michael to visit. After eating I lay in the bed with him on my lap watching cow videos on my phone. Michael has a way of lifting my spirits. What a joy to have an amazing little grandson, and what better incentive to get better and beat this Lyme disease.

During this hospital stay, I was fortunate to have a doctor who had previously practiced as a nephrologist or kidney specialist. He took special interest in my situation and dug deeper. He felt that I had kidney disease and insisted that I follow up with a practicing nephrologist. The kidney disease was troubling, of course, but I had one major concern during my hospital stay; I wanted to be released on Friday so I could be ready for opening day of whitetail deer season on Saturday. I was relieved when they sent me home Friday afternoon.

The next morning, I chose to hunt from the one tower that gives protection from the wind. My brother Ron in an amazing act of care, bought me a small gas heater to help me keep warm. I had a good day hunting, and as usual, was able to push through it. I returned home that evening to my 60th birthday party with extended family. Marlene surprised me by coming in from Kansas. The evening was filled with great conversation, holding Michael, and some meaningful gifts. Grateful, but exhausted, I fell into bed planning to be up early for church as usual.

On Monday I had another consult with Kim who wanted to follow up during this time of crisis. She suggested that I take two weeks off from treatment as I recovered from the acute illness. Later, when I met with my nephrologist, I was diagnosed with stage three kidney disease. Stage three is easy to live with and really has little effect on one's lifestyle.

However, I am fully aware that I do not want to get to stage four which really affects one's lifestyle or to stage five which requires dialysis.

As with so many diagnoses for Lyme disease patients, the root cause of the kidney disease was difficult to determine. It could simply be a result of living a number of years with one kidney. It could be a result of the treatment protocol, but I knew that Dr. Jemsek had been monitoring it closely, and my nephrologist assured me that the treatment should not have had a negative effect. It is also possible that my kidney disease was caused by the Lyme spirochetes which love all soft tissue. Dr. Jemsek has said it's possible it is a result of the Lyme disease, but the cause is not as important as the care for my precious kidney moving forward.

Kim had suggested in the November phone conversation that after a two week break from the treatment schedule, we would begin another two rounds of aggressive treatment for the babesia. I realized then that this would be a continued battle.

After the first round, I called a nurse with Jemsek's clinic to ask if there was an alternative to Mepron that I could take. I felt that I simply had met my end of that drug and could not do another round. She encouraged me to keep going and said there is an alternative, but the Mepron is the best medicine to overcome the babesia. I asked her if she had ever taken Mepron and knew what it was like. She said, "No, I have never taken it, but everyone who I know who has says that it's horrible." I told her that I agree with all the others. I also said I would be willing to take it this one more round, even though by this point Mepron was so difficult to get down, and I was so weary of living with its effect on my body and mind.

The work at church continued to be intense. As a pastoral team we were looking forward to the Christmas season and hoping the new year would give us a bit more normal schedule. Not only were we in the middle of the difficult discernment process through 2013-2014, but we were also nearing the completion of a major building renovation. As a team, we were exhausted and looking forward to a more relaxed pace.

Rest would have to be put on hold, however, as in January a 55-day revival happened in our community that required great energy and a lot of pastoral time during January and February.

The revival, called Revive Indiana, was a blessing to our congregation and community. I enjoyed my involvement, but was limited with how much I could participate because of my continued fatigue, headaches, and lightheadedness. Once again there were services that I wanted to be at, but I would have pressure headaches and just feel horrible overall. I'd wake up in the morning and know I needed to get to work, especially Saturday mornings when Revive was at our church, but all I wanted to do was stay in bed.

My fatigue continued to increase during times of long work hours and different stressors. This was actually a time of great frustration for me. It seemed I had been in treatment for so long, and I had expected to be much better by this point. There were many good things happening around me, and I wanted to be a part of them. While I was able to push through and be involved, I also was painfully aware that I was not keeping up with the other pastors. I was totally fed up with being the sick one and was determined not to talk with others about my increasing frustration and fatigue.

With the Revival time, I came face to face with another emotional part of a long treatment that seemed unending. There is a question that I know most Christians must confront at some time when they face chronic or terminal illnesses. *God, where are you?* This question is followed by random thoughts. *God, I need a miracle, and you seem absent. God, I know you have the power to heal me. I know that you love me and want what is best for me. So God, I am asking for complete healing, NOW.* These are thoughts and questions that as Christians we often do not think we can express. To express them can be interpreted as a lack of faith.

Yet, questions and thoughts such as these cut to the very center of our being. I think one fear we have is if we verbalize these questions we will get easy answers. These cliches do not satisfy the heart's longings. As a result, I remained silent.

At one of the revival meetings at our church a young woman with Lyme disease came into the service in a wheelchair. During the healing time, she received complete healing and was set free from her wheelchair. She literally was able to walk out of the church building being healed. I talked with her after the service and rejoiced with her. I honestly felt a great joy for her and her experience of healing, but I also must admit I wondered *why not me?* It was unsettling that it seemed like every person who knew I had Lyme disease was coming to me and telling me her story. I am not sure how they thought I should react to that news. Again, while I was glad for her, it was difficult to accept what I was experiencing. *Why does God heal some immediately and others through a long time of difficult treatment?* This is a question that I know has no good answer, but requires faith.

I have often said that if one could understand every circumstance and have all the answers, then we would not need to have faith. Faith steps in when we cannot make sense of what is happening. I have faith in the power and love of God. I do not know why He did not answer my prayers and the prayers of others in the way I desired. I do not have to understand, but I do find great comfort and hope in my faith that God is walking with me and carrying me, and ultimately is in control of my healing process. Hebrews 11: 1 *Faith is the confidence that what we hope for will actually happen; it gives us assurance about things we do not see.* (New Living Translation). *Faith gives us hope when we cannot see it.*

Philip Yancy, author of *What's So Amazing about Grace?* (1998), wrote that the kind of faith God values seems to develop best when everything fuzzes over, when God stays silent. *When the fog rolls in* is the phrase that comes to my mind. *When the fog rolls in.* I like that phrase. *When the fog rolls in* is an especially appropriate phrase when living with "brain fog." *When the fog rolls in* is when faith is tested, when faith carries us through. Those times when we cannot see clearly, God is with us. The times when we may be feeling the most desperate and our questions remain unanswered, God is with us. Those times when we wonder what the new day will bring, God is with us.

By faith, I believe in the healing power of God and know that I experience it in many moments and ways during my battle with Lyme disease. God did not give me quick, complete healing. But healing was coming, and the journey was both difficult and filled with joy.

I believe at this time I was feeling more depressed than at any point in my treatment. I had experienced some difficult moments before, but this was different. Mostly, I was so tired of the treatment and the disease. I was just so weary. For the first time, I was wondering if I would ever have a "normal life," whatever that means. I never questioned Dr. Jemsek, and I believed in the treatment, but it was not turning out as I had expected two years earlier.

Living Into It

The discernment process at our church was reaching its peak. I was involved in helping to start a new network of congregations. Revive Indiana was happening around me. My pastoral ministry was being stretched to the fullest, and in the midst of the joy and stress of my ministry, I was enduring a treatment that seemed endless. Just to add to the complications of our lives, Julie had major foot surgery and was the church's kitchen coordinator. On one good foot, she directed the food preparation and serving of over 1,000 people on Fridays and Saturdays for five weeks. And somehow, she managed to continue to care for me.

I felt so blessed by my life giving pastoral ministry, but at the same time I knew the stress and workload was affecting my ability to heal. In simple words, I just wanted to feel better so I could fulfill the deep call to pastor. There were many times when I cried out privately, *How long Lord, how long?* What I didn't realize was that I truly was ending the worst part of my treatment and much better days were close at hand. It is true the darkest part of the night is just before sunrise. Thank you, Jesus.

March and April of 2015 I began to experience real improvement. I still had fatigue and required naps on the antibiotic weeks. I still also had right eye pressure and pressure headaches, but I came to realize that the headaches were worse during times of stress. When on treatment I had some lightheadedness, but on my recovery weeks felt much better. Pain and fatigue did not seem constant, and I started to feel just a little bit in control.

I went to the April appointment with Kim with one main objective. I was determined to tell her that I was done with treatment. It had now been over two years, and I was so physically and emotionally done. Since I was feeling better during my recovery weeks, I felt certain that if I was off of treatment I would feel good all the time. When she examined me and said that my liver was still a bit enlarged, I knew I was toast. She began to write up a protocol for the next months of treatment, and I stopped her and said I didn't want to do any more. We began to discuss it further, and she said she would go see if Dr. Jemsek could join us.

After a few minutes they walked in together, and I knew that I would give in. Dr. Jemsek checked my liver and agreed with her assessment. He then began to explain to me that they were finding it was so critical to get the babesia under full control before ending treatment. He felt confident that if I were to stop now I would probably regress at some point, probably in just a few months. They both encouraged me to hang in there a bit longer. I agreed without hesitation at that point. I did insist that I would not take any more Mepron; I could not face that anymore and wanted the alternative. They agreed to prescribe that for me.

In her notes Kim remarked: "Julie's support, as always, is apparent." While I was reaching my end of coping ability with the treatment, Julie was prepared and desired to go the distance. Not once did she suggest she had had all she could take, even after years of carrying me through weeks of antibiotics and spending hours upon hours figuring out, ordering, and organizing medications. We returned home with the hope that when we returned in August we would get the good news that I was ready for the maintenance protocol.

Through the summer I continued to improve. During the weeks of treatment I would have some bad days, but mostly good ones. I went through four more months of intensive treatment for babesia and tolerated it quite well. There were no major stressor events that summer, although I went with our youth group to the church assembly in Kansas City. While there I could not keep up with the sponsors and the late nights. Still, I was able to be helpful. In addition, I had a torn cartilage in my knee which slowed me down. We were also in the process of searching for a new youth pastor which required extra time and energy. Overall, even though the stressors weren't completely gone, life seemed very good.

In August of 2015, we returned for an appointment with Dr. Jemsek. After an evaluation where he was satisfied with the state of my liver he told me the wonderful news that he believed I was ready to move to the maintenance schedule. What wonderful words to hear! It was different, not as emotional as almost three years earlier when Kim had told me she was 100% sure I had Lyme and that they could help me, but it had truly been a long and difficult journey and "maintenance" felt like victory. The hardest part of the journey was behind me, and I was overjoyed.

In his report Dr. Jemsek wrote, "This is a pleasant, tan, adult male looking much younger than his stated age and physically fit." He was always so kind in his reports, and I had grown to deeply appreciate his caring presence and expertise. Through his wisdom and treatment I was finding healing. That evening Julie and I went out to eat in a nice restaurant and had a more appropriate celebration than I had fourteen months earlier. No potato chips.

Part of the good news of the end of treatment was that it made it possible to go on a moose and elk hunt in British Columbia in September with my son Casey. It was something we had been planning for over a year since I had taken for granted that the treatment would be over long before. I had gone to the appointment prepared to tell Dr. Jemsek that I needed a month break to go on the hunt if treatment were to continue.

True to form, I had another complication just before the hunt. I finally was able to have the surgery for the torn cartilage in my knee along with two stress fractures. The surgery was only eight days before a five-day truck trip across Canada and fourteen days before the hunt. I had a lot of pain struggling through the woods in pursuit of a moose, but when I was successful it was all well worth it. On top of that, Casey got an elk, so it was a great hunt. Even more special was the time I could spend with him.

In November and December I felt that I was regressing a bit and became concerned. I was able to get an appointment in January with a new practitioner in Dr. Jemsek's clinic, Kelly. Although, this was the first time we met with her it was obvious she had spent careful time studying my case and was well prepared to meet with me. She noted that I was appropriately discouraged with even a slight increase in my symptoms. I was having trouble sleeping and feeling more fatigue.

After her many questions, she was prepared to give me a lecture. It felt like I had driven a long way to just be told, "Why have you not been doing what we asked you to do?" I replied that after the treatment ended I was just so done, and I just stopped doing the things I knew I needed to be doing such as detox regimens, using my CPAP, and avoiding stress. Instead, I had been spending time in the woods, diving back into work, and enjoying the spontaneity of life unmeasured by pills, IVs, and naps.

She reminded me that I had to continue doing the detox things they suggested in order to maintain a lower level of inflammation. She insisted that I start using my CPAP again so that I could get a deeper sleep that was required to have a healthy body and higher immune function. She got the message through my thick skull, and I returned determined to do as I was told.

One kind lady in our congregation who followed my progress and with whom I was completely honest—actually Julie was more honest with her—sent me a card with the following message: "As pastor you must hope people in the congregation follow what you say better than you follow your doctor's instructions." Point well taken.

Part of the discussion with Kelly included her questioning my sense of how to manage stress and workload. Again, I insisted that with the end of treatment I felt I should be able to handle a normal life of pastoring. I was unsure why stress or workload would be an issue at this point.

She said that I have to understand that I am not healed, but that the maintenance period is a time of healing. She questioned if I had allowed myself the time and space to heal.

Julie and I both knew that I had not. I decided to request the congregational oversight board to allow me to move my upcoming sabbatical from the fall to the spring and summer. I was convinced that I needed time away from the regular demands of pastoral ministry to allow time and space for continued healing. As was always the case, the board immediately approved my request. I was and still am constantly amazed and grateful for the full support of our church's board and pastoral team. The congregation was also fully supportive of giving me this gift.

The encouragement and love of the congregation is represented in the vast number of cards I've received, at least 420 cards with 94 of them coming from one dear supporter, Ann. Her cards were all handmade and carried a simple but profound handwritten message. As the treatment process grew longer her cards came weekly. I am not the type of person who sends cards, but these messages of support and hope have been so meaningful to me in this journey. The folks of Clinton Frame Church will never fully understand how important their support was and is in my healing process.

During this sabbatical, I started writing my illness narrative, and writing has brought its own kind of healing. Writing does not take away the illness, but it is a powerful reminder of the amazing journey I have been on the last 16 years. From ages 46 to 62 my health has been compromised by the bite of a small tick. Writing this story has also reminded me of the many God moments in this journey and how impossible it would have been without God, family, church, and friends.

These days I am trying to develop a new normal. I really don't know how a 61-year-old man should feel as I have not had a typical journey since age 46. I pray that more strength will return. I honestly do not feel that I have the strength and stamina that I should. I still require more sleep than I think I should need, and when I push and push, I crash and need to rest. But, I am not complaining as I feel so much better now than I did when I was 50.

I have more hope for the future and look forward to experiencing even more recovery over the next year. Life is good, and I feel good. I love being with my family, especially my two wonderful grandchildren, Michael and Julia, who bring so much joy. I am so glad that I have the energy to truly enjoy life each day.

While I'm writing this, Julie and I have been in Colorado as a time away before I return to work in less than two weeks. Today our son Casey joined me, and we hiked Quandry, a 14,265-foot peak in the Breckenridge area with more than a 3,000-foot elevation gain. After wanting to make this climb for more than six years, we summited in just over three hours. The feat represented a small victory over Lyme disease. This hike was only possible because of my continuing recovery, and the ability to do it was indeed a mountaintop experience. A person who has recovered from the debilitating presence of the Lyme bacteria said, "I have my life back again." This is how I feel. I have my life back again.

Since I know there is no "cure" for Lyme disease, especially for a person who has been infected as long as me, I will need to find my new normal and live into it. I pray that I will never regress and need to return to a treatment protocol, but if I do, I know the doctor who will help me face it and find health again.

No matter what the future holds, I rest assured that my very special wife is vigilant, and for some reason seems determined to keep me around. As one of my brothers-in-laws says, "Julie is a good one to have on your side."

Julie and I agree that life the past seventeen years has been really difficult. We wonder sometimes what other couples do with all their free time, as the hours and days we have spent seeing doctors and hospitals would surely add up to at least a year or two. We would not be honest if we did not acknowledge that at times we feel robbed of some great empty nest years.

Our extra days in D.C. to visit museums and historical sites before or after appointments have added fun memories to challenging times. Occasionally we call up Julie's cousin Rennette—who led us to Dr. Jemsek—and her husband Mike to meet for dinner. Family and friends who have made parts of this journey with us add so much love to our lives.

It is difficult to know all the ways this journey has changed us. We certainly have taken on a seriousness to life, and we are much more empathetic to others with chronic illness. There is sadness for both of us.

Still, we are trying to focus on more laughter and joy, especially with our wonderful family. Our faith in God is really what sustains us in the hardest times. We both came from Christian homes where our parents instilled in us to trust in God and to have a positive outlook on life. Julie regularly says she is grateful we have a very close and loving relationship, as the reality of a chronic illness can do much harm in a marriage. Through it all, we both believe we can truly say that we have become fuller soulmates because of it.

With God's grace, Julie and I are on this journey side by side. In our 2013 Christmas letter to friends and family, at the end of the ten months of IV treatment, Julie wrote the following:

223 bags of IV antibiotics
101 bags of Lactated Ringers

2 line infections with 3 days of hospitalization each

Hundreds of oral antibiotic pills (too many to count)

Countless lab tests, almost weekly

10 months of anti-malarial medication

I think thousands of nutraceuticals, enzymes, probiotics, herbals

Removal of central line in November

More energy – noteworthy, but still improvement needed

Neuropathy in feet for 7 years. Gone!

Constant neck and back pain. Gone!

Pressure headaches behind right eye. Gone!

Brain fog improving.

A normal heart rate.

Working 40 plus hours weekly again.

Days ahead may or may not hold similar lists. We cannot know. But truly, I am blessed and have so much to be thankful for. I am at peace with a God who loves and cares for me.

Epilogue

We don't measure God's love through life's circumstances,
we measure life's circumstances through God's love.
-Craig Groeschel, "When God Doesn't Make Sense" (2015)

I finished writing the main part of this narrative in July of 2016, the day I summited the 14,265 foot Quandry peak with Casey. By the end of August I could tell I was regressing and the symptoms of Lyme disease returning.

Naturally, a major part of that return was fatigue along with pressure headaches and numbness in my feet, right arm, and hand. One sure sign was when I got my bow out to begin to practice and prepare for the fall archery season. Even before I got to the closet I knew I would not be able to pull the bow to full draw. As expected, my arm was too weak. I put the bow back in the closet and drove to a local hunting supply store to buy a crossbow. There was no way that this disease was going to cause me to miss my favorite time of hunting for a third time.

Mid-September Julie and I made a trip to D.C. to meet with our still favorite physician assistant, Kim Fogarty. In her initial poking and prodding she found that my liver and spleen were slightly enlarged again which meant the co-infection babesia was active again. As was always the case with her, she was very thorough in her examination and asked probing questions. I answered them with a sense of dread, because I had a clear idea of what was to come.

So I was not surprised with what she found and her recommendation that I return to treatment. The treatment would not be as aggressive as the earlier treatments, so I told myself that maybe I could do this and continue working full-time. But, in my heart I knew I needed to resign. In my disappointment, I was not willing to face that reality until weeks later. Julie and I really did not talk much about the result of the appointment on the 10-hour drive home. She knew I was angry, and as always gave me the space I needed to process.

Upon returning home Julie continued to do research and was reading a couple of new books about Lyme disease. She was careful to not push me, but I knew that she was thinking it was time for me to resign as pastor. My emotions were a mess as I was battling my own thoughts about what I knew I needed to do, but was not quite ready to give up. For 23 years, my identity had been as a pastor at Clinton Frame. That was an identity and ministry that I did not want to let go of.

After we were home about a week Julie traveled with her mom and sister to Nicaragua to visit one of our nieces and her husband. She was gone a week and continued to read *Insights into Lyme Disease Treatment*, the one book on Lyme that she had taken with her. This book is a compilation of "13 Lyme-Literate Care Practitioners Sharing Their Healing Strategies." Most of these practitioners were clear that it is very difficult for persons with long-term chronic Lyme to heal without a lifestyle change. More specifically, they insist that in most cases for the condition to improve an individual must let go of full-time employment and live as stress-free a life as possible for an extended period of time. In a phone conversation,

Julie said she was reading some new and interesting research on Lyme and we needed to talk when she got home. I was pretty sure what she meant.

My first step in my discernment process was to return to my Spiritual Director who had helped me cope and face spiritual issues through some of the most difficult years of illness and treatment. He had given me wise supportive counsel in the past, and now I needed to talk with him about how to discern my way forward. After an hour of discussion and opening up my feelings to him, he had a simple but profound suggestion: Write a brief letter to the congregational oversight board offering my resignation. Keep it for two to three weeks and discern how the letter makes me feel. If it feels right after that time, offer it to them. I told him that I already knew I would feel a deep relief to not have to continue working through treatment. That way, I knew I could allow myself the time and space to beat this disease.

I wrote the letter the next day and knew immediately what I would do. Julie returned from Nicaragua and had underlined places in her book for me to read. Through more reading, talking with Julie, and admitting what was on my heart, I knew the only good way forward was to resign. As I was processing, I had a phone consult with Dr. Lee. After reviewing my blood work he said, "You are still working full-time aren't you?" "You might want to rethink that." I told him I was planning on offering my resignation and he responded that would be a good idea. I waited several weeks until the next board meeting to offer it to them. They accepted it very graciously while speaking words of affirmation. This congregational oversight board is a group of people I have come to depend on, and I can count on them to always put my best interest first.

Those first days and weeks of knowing I was resigning held a strong mixture of emotions. I felt tremendous relief to be able to set a date when I would not be working and taking treatment at the same time. But this relief was accompanied by intense sadness. The five Sunday mornings when I knew I was resigning, but the congregation was unaware, I had many tears through the songs we would sing. I would be thinking how can Julie and I leave this community? Fortunately, since I sat on the front row, the only person who could see the tears was Julie, and she understood.

After one pastoral care call with a dear older couple in the church, I had tears almost all the way home. This was repeated a number of times. Even though it hurt, I was determined and knew it was the best option. I had come to acknowledge and accept that I would not heal from Lyme until I let go of a pastoral ministry I loved and cherished.

On the last Sunday in November, at the end of worship, I announced my resignation to the congregation. Through my tears I could see shock on the faces of people I love, and I could see that many of them had tears as well. It is impossible to explain the pain and the relief of that moment. The congregation gathered around Julie and me, and the prayer and hugs were powerful and healing. I was so glad that now the congregation knew, and we could move on and make plans for the future.

Along with the board, I set my last date of pastoral ministry at Clinton Frame Church to be March 26, 2017. As I am writing this, I still have five weeks until that date. I have experienced overwhelming support and understanding from the people of Clinton Frame. There have been many moments of interaction that cause me to repeat the earlier question. How can Julie and I leave a community of faith that we have grown to appreciate in so many ways?

To my amazement, the board has asked Julie and me to remain a part of the congregation after March 26th. I understand how unusual this is and have some knowledge of the possible pitfalls of a pastor staying after resigning. But, I believe we can walk through the coming months together and make it good for Julie and me and for the congregation.

The last series of sermons I preached were titled: "When God does not make sense." The idea for the series came from Craig Groeschel. The first week was "When it seems God is not listening." When God is silent it does not mean God is absent. The second week was "When God shows up late." When God shows up, He will not meet our expectations; He will exceed them. And the final week "When it seems God is uncooperative." When our prayers are not answered as we hoped for, can we continue to trust God and hear these words: My grace is sufficient for you, for my power is made perfect in weakness.

I am fully aware that pastors must guard against sermons being therapy sessions for themselves, but the response from the congregation through this series was overwhelmingly positive. For me, preparing and delivering the sermons was both challenging and healing. I could see my own experience with Lyme in each sermon, but of course, I also saw much more.

The text for the series was Hebrews 11:1—Faith is being certain of what we hope for, and confident in the things we cannot see. The future is uncertain for me; there is uncertainty when it comes to my health. I have faith that healing will come with continued treatment and a change in lifestyle. I do not know what the new normal will be for me a year from now, but I have faith that life will be good. The sermon series brought me back to a phrase that has been my guide the last number of years through congregational discernment and my own life journey: We walk by faith.

When the fog rolls in, we walk by faith. Not alone, but together.

Afterward (a.k.a Ticked)

I was told at the beginning of my treatment that there is no cure, especially since I had been infected with the disease for as many years as I had. The goal was to rid my body of enough of the bacteria from the Lyme and to boost my immune system to the point where I could live a "normal" life, but I would never be "cured" of the Lyme. While I was not surprised to hear the words "no cure," it is still a devastating prognosis.

Lyme disease has been reported in every state except Hawaii, and in at least 30 countries. One of the fastest spreading vector-borne infections, Lyme disease begins with a simple tick bite.

In 2013, The Center for Disease Control (CDC) increased the estimated number of new cases each year from 30,000 to 300,000. In 2016, that estimate was 329,000. Yet, to date, there are no reliable diagnostic tools and no definitive cures for those who suffer from chronic Lyme disease. This must change.

Raising awareness and educating people about chronic Lyme disease is a critical step. Sharing my narrative contributes to that effort, but so too can a few concrete details about the disease and the history of Lyme.

In the 1960s and early 70s a group of children and adults in Lyme, Connecticut and the surrounding area were experiencing puzzling and debilitating health issues. Their symptoms included swollen knees, arthritic-like joint pain, paralysis, headaches, skin rashes, and chronic fatigue. The one commonality among these people who suffered a variety of symptoms was they had all been bitten by a tick. The doctors had no answers for these mysterious symptoms.

In the early 1970s the CDC sent researchers to Connecticut to evaluate the outbreak of disabling arthritis among children. In time, they suspected that an unidentified infectious agent was the culprit and reasoned it may be tick-borne due to the recurring theme of patients' reports of tick bites. In 1977, it was termed Lyme Arthritis, and by 1979 after further study, the researchers realized that there were a great many more symptoms to this illness than inflammatory arthritis. The name was changed to "Lyme disease" and claimed as a new clinical entity. The name continued to reference the small town of the first outbreak, while also acknowledging its more pervasive impact.

While the CDC recognizes that there are more than 300,000 new cases of Lyme disease each year, they will only acknowledge it in its initial stage. In the very early stages of the disease, literally within 40 days of the tick bite, treatment is easy and highly successful. This is why when one is bitten by a tick, and especially if there is a rash, the blood test must be done immediately and antibiotic treatment administered right away. Caught and treated in its very early stages Lyme disease is easily cured.

When not cured at the earliest onset of the disease the Lyme bacteria spirals deep into any soft tissue and becomes difficult to diagnose and treat.

For some reason the CDC and the Infectious Disease Society of America (IDSA) refuse to acknowledge that chronic Lyme disease exists. I believe this is more the fault of the board of IDSA who through their power have kept the CDC in check. Both the IDSA and CDC speak in terms of post-Lyme syndrome, basically insisting that when it is not caught in the initial stage over time it simply disappears. This is simply not true. The hundreds of thousands of patients who suffer from the incredibly long-lasting and debilitating effects of chronic Lyme know this is not true.

There is no way for me to know for sure why the IDSA and CDC have turned their backs on chronic Lyme patients, but at the heart of the issue may be money and politics. Some of the persons on the IDSA board have direct connections with insurance and pharmaceutical companies. I don't know the answer, but I do know that the medical establishment under the guidelines set by the IDSA and the CDC have failed those who suffer from chronic Lyme.

There is much I do not understand about the whole arena of chronic Lyme disease and how it has been handled by the medical establishment and our government. To date, our government has provided little resourcing for the research that is needed in order to find good diagnostic tests and treatment for Lyme. I am aware that for many years our government dedicated more than $3 billion in public funding annually for research to find solutions for HIV/AIDS. This support peaked in the 1990s and was successful in providing great help to those who were affected by this terrible disease.

In contrast, all of the research currently being done on chronic Lyme disease is private pay, as our government is not willing to give dollars to find a solution. But, why would they give money to find a solution for a disease that the IDSA and CDC continue to say does not exist? At the same time, why does our government continue to accept what the medical establishment is saying when there is so much evidence to the contrary? Obviously, I have many unanswered questions.

An even larger scandal for me is how medically-trained physicians, who seek to treat patients of chronic Lyme disease, are often sued by insurance companies and have their credentials taken away by State

Medical Boards. I personally know one doctor who was sued by Blue Cross and Blue Shield and his license suspended by his State Medical Board, simply because he treats patients suffering from chronic Lyme. His clinic was closed down, and he had to relocate to another location to continue to treat patients living with Lyme.

But there is some hope that such practices may change. Today at least twelve states have legislation in place or pending, which either protects Lyme-treating physicians and/or mandates insurance coverage. Most of these states are in the northeast with the last state that I am aware of being Virginia. Is it not troubling that states must pass legislation in order to protect doctors who treat Lyme patients and mandate insurance companies to cover their treatment? It is obvious to me that something is horribly wrong with this picture.

Again, I don't know the answers to the many questions about why Lyme disease diagnosis and treatment remain unsupported, but part of the result of not knowing the truth are conspiracy theories. I am not one who is quick to believe such theories, but when it feels like the truth is being kept from the public eye, conspiracy theories abound.

I will briefly present just one conspiracy theory. It is the one that I have heard the most often. I don't know if it is true; in fact, I find it hard to believe. But in the absence of the truth it is hard to know what to believe. The most prevalent conspiracy theory is the Plum Island theory.

The Plum Island theory went mainstream with Michael Carroll's 2004 book *Lab 257: The Disturbing Story of the Government's Secret Plum Island Germ Laboratory*. This theory is believed by many because Plum Island is located off the coast of Long Island, New York and is close to Lyme, Connecticut, the site of the first known Lyme disease outbreak in the U.S. As an animal disease center, Plum Island has been at the center of many dark government conspiracies of top secret biological weapon experimentation back to era of the Cold War.

Because of its location and known work in biological warfare, the

Plum Island conspiracy theory has taken off and many people believe it. Many believe that Lyme disease was being tested as a possible biological weapon, and somehow it escaped the island and into the general population.

Again, is it true or not? But, for some reason, the medical establishment led by the IDSA board and the CDC continue to refuse to acknowledge chronic Lyme. Tragically, our government refuses to fund research into Lyme disease, even though it is devastating to the lives of so many.

When I asked a leading expert in the area of Lyme disease how he believes Lyme came into being in the United States, he simply said, "All I will say is that someone was messing with something they should not have been messing with." To date, that is the best answer I have found.

Our government is responsible to protect the health and safety of our people, and most times they do. But in this case, they are not. To illustrate, I'll compare the response to Lyme disease with our government's and the CDCs response to the Zika virus.

The recent Zika virus is spread through the bite of a mosquito. While some people have no symptoms at all, it causes mild illness in others. The CDC has made a link between Zika infection during pregnancy and resulting devastating birth defects. I think we would all agree that we need to do what we can to stop the spread of this dangerous infection to unborn babies. And our government's response was to encourage all of us to remain vigilant when it comes to combating the spread of diseases like Zika. This is why President Obama called on Congress to provide emergency funding to combat the disease in a variety of forms: speed the development of a vaccine; make testing more accessible and results prompt, especially for pregnant women; ensure that states and communities—especially those in the south—have the resources they need to fight the mosquito that carries the virus. The Senate then voted to advance $1.2 billion to an emergency fund to combat the Zika virus. This was less than the $1.9 billion the President requested.

The CDC Foundation put out this plea: "Together, we can stop Zika." Tom Frieden, the CDC Director, wrote: "Never before have we had a mosquito-borne infection that can cause serious birth defects on a large scale. There is an urgent need to learn more and do more—and all of us have a role to play." Following the call for each of us to play a part, he pleaded for financial contributions to support further CDC research and testing.

I absolutely have no issue with the urgent appeal to find answers to the Zika virus. I fully support it. But, I wonder why nothing has been done or is being done for chronic Lyme disease.

The fact is that chronic Lyme has affected hundreds of thousands of adults in the United States and many children as well. Many believe that Lyme disease crosses the uterine wall and infects unborn babies. These persons are being neglected by our government policies and the larger medical community.

There are many people today who are trying to work at creating political awareness, and I am grateful for those who are dedicating their lives to finding solutions for people who are suffering. A number of support networks and advocacy groups for people with chronic Lyme also provide critical support. The International Lyme and Associated Disease Society (ILADS) is working at research and developing better testing options. But, all of this is done with no assistance from the IDSA, CDC, and government policy. In fact, when the ILADS presented a much more effective approach to testing and diagnosing chronic Lyme disease, the IDSA refused to listen and insisted that the techniques developed by them in 2004 are sufficient.

I simply believe that it is outrageous the IDSA continues to stand with the old techniques. Due to the power of the IDSA the much more effective diagnostic tools and treatment put out by the ILADS cannot be used in the United States.

For a person infected with chronic Lyme to receive help requires three things: money, time, and a support system. I know that this is absolutely true from experience. I had the great blessing of financial resources to pay doctors out-of-pocket, to pay for expensive treatment, and to pay travel expenses. I had the blessing of being able to cut back hours at work and have a flexible schedule. I had the most important blessing of a supportive family, church, and an incredible wife who is a nurse, and the most determined woman I know. She will not give up on me.

When I think of my own health history, it is telling to compare my experience of being treated for chronic Lyme versus being treated for renal cell carcinoma (kidney cancer). I was diagnosed with cancer through a simple test and the test result was accurate. I was treated by a local qualified physician and had the surgery at the local hospital. My insurance company paid for the full amount of the treatment without question. When I told people I had cancer they believed me and understood the seriousness of my condition.

With Lyme disease I never had a 'medically accepted' positive diagnosis from a test. To get treatment, I had to travel to Florida and then Washington D.C. to meet with incredibly successful doctors who are not recognized by the medical establishment and chose to work outside of the establishment. I had to explain to people that the diagnosis and treatment for my condition are very controversial and varied. I had to pay out-of-pocket for all the doctor visits, and the expensive part of the treatment, because my insurance company would not.

A person being treated for chronic Lyme said that she lived with an invisible disease. While she looked well on the outside, inside she felt like she was dying. I totally identify with that statement. I lived with the thought that many people question if I am really sick. Honestly, I struggled with that same thought myself. It seems much easier to deal with an illness that is medically accepted, has accurate diagnostic tools, and has well-known treatment protocols.

Supportive and knowledgeable people have been our most valuable allies, but several other sources are also noteworthy. The *Lyme Times,* a magazine published quarterly by LymeDisease.org, and available on the website itself, is one of the most reliable and reader-friendly sources on Lyme disease. LymeDisease.org provides grassroots advocacy on a local and national level. They are paying for research, fighting for access to appropriate medical care, and advocating for change in the political arena. They have also initiated the largest patient-based research to date.

The International Lyme and Associated Diseases Society (www.ilads. org), the advocacy group mentioned earlier, is in the forefront of the war for Lyme awareness. They are working in the political arena, organizing conferences for physician education and raising awareness about Lyme.

The Jemsek Specialty Clinic website also has excellent information on Lyme. There are more books and resources on Lyme disease available now than three years ago when I began treatment, and we have read a number of them. Some of the ones I've found most helpful include *Why Can't I get Better? Solving the Mystery of Lyme and Chronic Disease* by Richard Horowitz, *Natural Treatments for Lyme Coinfections* by Stephen Harrod Buhner, *Beyond Lyme Disease* by Connie Strasheim, *Insight into Lyme Disease Treatment* also by Connie Strasheim, and for humor, which all Lyme patients need, *Lyme Loonies* by David Skidmore.

The Documentary Under Our Skin which came out in 2008 can be purchased on DVD. It is a must watch to understand the disease and the political and medical barriers that patients and doctors face. There is also available now a follow-up documentary *Under our skin 2 Emergence,* (2014) that extends this conversation into more recent years.

The more we learn about Lyme disease the more frustrated Julie and I become. And we are not alone. A quote from Kenneth B. Liegner, MD in chapter one of *Lyme Loonies* (2015) by David Skidmore sums it up:

> *In the fullness of time, the mainstream handling of chronic Lyme disease will be viewed as one of the most shameful episodes in the history of medicine because elements of academic medicine, elements of Government,*

and virtually the entire insurance industry have colluded to deny a disease. This has resulted in the needless suffering of many individuals who deteriorate and sometimes die for lack of timely application of treatment or denial of treatment beyond some arbitrary duration.

_____

from Julie:

When Terry was first diagnosed with Lyme, we had no idea of the unethical controversies that shroud this disease. It has been over 45 years since it became public, and very little has been done by the medical establishment.

I believe that the refusal to deal with Lyme disease will become in time a medical tragedy and embarrassment to our medical healthcare system. Many sources speak of Lyme as being in epidemic proportions. According to the medical world, Chronic Lyme is non-existent. Apparently, if not treated, the Lyme bacteria will magically disappear and the disease is gone. Really?

Hundreds of thousands of patients suffering unimaginably will bet otherwise. Medical insurance and doctors deny care based on a scandal coming from powers at the top. Physicians such as Dr. Jemsek, who follow their Hippocratic Oath of 'do no harm' and treat patients with care and dignity, are truly some of the most courageous heroes out there.

_____

Even in our frustration we know we have much to be grateful for. Through this journey we've met amazing people who were present to provide care and medical expertise. We are grateful for successful treatment and are thankful for those who offered support and encouragement at times when Terry wanted to give up. With so much to be thankful for we could never become bitter.

We believe with all our hearts that the hundreds of thousands of people suffering from chronic Lyme disease deserve better care and treatment.

We encourage you to donate to one of these organizations that are on the forefront of Lyme research and education.

Ilads.org
lymedisease.org

One hundred percent of the proceeds of this book will be donated to the above organizations.